Publisher's Note

We are delighted to bring you the 2011 Past Papers and you will see that we have changed the format from previous editions. As part of our environmental awareness strategy, we have attempted to make these new editions as sustainable as possible.

To do this, we have printed on white paper and bound the answer sections into the book. This not only allows us to use significantly less paper but we are also, for the first time, able to source all the materials from sustainable sources.

We hope you like the new editions and by purchasing this product, you are not only supporting an independent Scottish publishing company but you are also, in the International Year of Forests, not contributing to the destruction of the world's forests.

Thank you for your support and please see the following websites for more information to support the above statement –

www.fsc-uk.org

www.loveforests.com

© Scottish Qualifications Authority

First exam published in 2007.
Published by Bright Red Publishing Ltd, 6 Stafford Street, Edinburgh EH3 7AU
tel: 0131 220 5804 fax: 0131 220 6710 info@brightredpublishing.co.uk www.brightredpublishing.co.uk

ISBN 978-1-84948-224-0

A CIP Catalogue record for this book is available from the British Library.

Bright Red Publishing is grateful to the copyright holders, as credited on the final page of the Question Section, for permission to use their material. Every effort has been made to trace the copyright holders and to obtain their permission for the use of copyright material. Bright Red Publishing will be happy to receive information allowing us to rectify any error or omission in future editions.

OFFICIAL SQA PAST PAPERS
WITH ANSWERS

HIGHER

PHYSICS
2007-2011

ALIS
1288644

SQA

BrightRED
PUBLISHING

HIGHER

2007

[BLANK PAGE]

72.2%

X069/301

NATIONAL
QUALIFICATIONS
2007

WEDNESDAY, 16 MAY
1.00 PM – 3.30 PM

PHYSICS
HIGHER

Read Carefully

Reference may be made to the Physics Data Booklet.

1 All questions should be attempted.

Section A (questions 1 to 20)

2 Check that the answer sheet is for Physics Higher (Section A).

3 For this section of the examination you must use an **HB pencil** and, where necessary, an eraser.

4 Check that the answer sheet you have been given has **your name**, **date of birth**, **SCN** (Scottish Candidate Number) and **Centre Name** printed on it.
   Do not change any of these details.

5 If any of this information is wrong, tell the Invigilator immediately.

6 If this information is correct, **print** your name and seat number in the boxes provided.

7 There is **only one correct** answer to each question.

8 Any rough working should be done on the question paper or the rough working sheet, **not** on your answer sheet.

9 At the end of the exam, put the **answer sheet for Section A inside the front cover of your answer book**.

10 Instructions as to how to record your answers to questions 1–20 are given on page three.

Section B (questions 21 to 31)

11 Answer the questions numbered 21 to 31 in the answer book provided.

12 **All answers must be written clearly and legibly in ink**.

13 Fill in the details on the front of the answer book.

14 Enter the question number clearly in the margin of the answer book beside each of your answers to questions 21 to 31.

15 Care should be taken to give an appropriate number of significant figures in the final answers to calculations.

16 Where additional paper, eg square ruled paper, is used, write your name and SCN (Scottish Candidate Number) on it and place it inside the front cover of your answer booklet.

SCOTTISH
QUALIFICATIONS
AUTHORITY

DATA SHEET
COMMON PHYSICAL QUANTITIES

Quantity	Symbol	Value	Quantity	Symbol	Value
Speed of light in vacuum	c	$3 \cdot 00 \times 10^8$ m s^{-1}	Mass of electron	m_e	$9 \cdot 11 \times 10^{-31}$ kg
Magnitude of the charge on an electron	e	$1 \cdot 60 \times 10^{-19}$ C	Mass of neutron	m_n	$1 \cdot 675 \times 10^{-27}$ kg
Gravitational acceleration on Earth	g	$9 \cdot 8$ m s^{-2}	Mass of proton	m_p	$1 \cdot 673 \times 10^{-27}$ kg
Planck's constant	h	$6 \cdot 63 \times 10^{-34}$ J s			

REFRACTIVE INDICES
The refractive indices refer to sodium light of wavelength 589 nm and to substances at a temperature of 273 K.

Substance	Refractive index	Substance	Refractive index
Diamond	2·42	Water	1·33
Crown glass	1·50	Air	1·00

SPECTRAL LINES

Element	Wavelength/nm	Colour	Element	Wavelength/nm	Colour
Hydrogen	656	Red	Cadmium	644	Red
	486	Blue-green		509	Green
	434	Blue-violet		480	Blue
	410	Violet		Lasers	
	397	Ultraviolet	Element	Wavelength/nm	Colour
	389	Ultraviolet	Carbon dioxide	9550 } 10590 }	Infrared
Sodium	589	Yellow	Helium-neon	633	Red

PROPERTIES OF SELECTED MATERIALS

Substance	Density/ kg m^{-3}	Melting Point/ K	Boiling Point/ K
Aluminium	$2 \cdot 70 \times 10^3$	933	2623
Copper	$8 \cdot 96 \times 10^3$	1357	2853
Ice	$9 \cdot 20 \times 10^2$	273	. . . .
Sea Water	$1 \cdot 02 \times 10^3$	264	377
Water	$1 \cdot 00 \times 10^3$	273	373
Air	$1 \cdot 29$	. . . .	. . . .
Hydrogen	$9 \cdot 0 \times 10^{-2}$	14	20

The gas densities refer to a temperature of 273 K and a pressure of $1 \cdot 01 \times 10^5$ Pa.

SECTION A

For questions 1 to 20 in this section of the paper the answer to each question is either A, B, C, D or E. Decide what your answer is, then, using your pencil, put a horizontal line in the space provided—see the example below.

EXAMPLE

The energy unit measured by the electricity meter in your home is the

    A kilowatt-hour

    B ampere

    C watt

    D coulomb

    E volt.

The correct answer is **A**—kilowatt-hour. The answer **A** has been clearly marked in **pencil** with a horizontal line (see below).

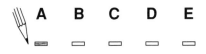

Changing an answer

If you decide to change your answer, carefully erase your first answer and, using your pencil, fill in the answer you want. The answer below has been changed to **E**.

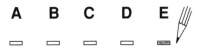

[Turn over

SECTION A

Answer questions 1–20 on the answer sheet.

1. Which row shows both quantities classified correctly?

	Scalar	Vector
A	weight	force
B	force	mass
C	mass	distance
D	distance	momentum
E	momentum	time

2. A ball is thrown vertically upwards and falls back to Earth. Neglecting air resistance, which velocity-time graph represents its motion?

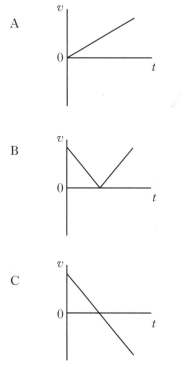

A

B

C

D

E

3. A person stands on a weighing machine in a lift. When the lift is at rest, the reading on the machine is 700 N. The lift now descends and its speed increases at a constant rate. The reading on the machine

   A   is a constant value higher than 700 N

   B   is a constant value lower than 700 N

   C   continually increases from 700 N

   D   continually decreases from 700 N

   E   remains constant at 700 N.

4. Momentum can be measured in

   A $N\,kg^{-1}$

   B $N\,m$

   C $N\,m\,s^{-1}$

   D $kg\,m\,s^{-1}$

   E $kg\,m\,s^{-2}$.

5. A cannon of mass 2000 kg fires a cannonball of mass 5·00 kg.

   The cannonball leaves the cannon with a speed of $50·0\,m\,s^{-1}$.

   The speed of the cannon immediately after firing is

   A $0·125\,m\,s^{-1}$

   B $8·00\,m\,s^{-1}$

   C $39·9\,m\,s^{-1}$

   D $40·1\,m\,s^{-1}$

   E $200\,m\,s^{-1}$.

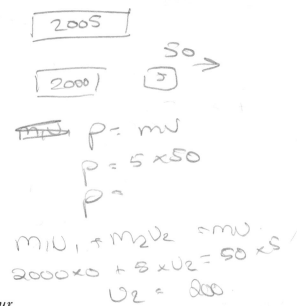

6. The graph shows the force acting on an object of mass 5·0 kg.

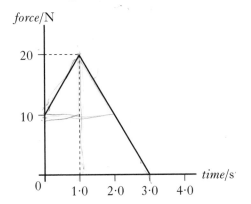

The change in the object's momentum is

A   7·0 kg m s^{-1}

B   30 kg m s^{-1}

C   35 kg m s^{-1}

D   60 kg m s^{-1}

E   175 kg m s^{-1}.

7. Which of the following gives the approximate relative spacings of molecules in ice, water and water vapour?

	Spacing of molecules in ice	Spacing of molecules in water	Spacing of molecules in water vapour
A	1	1	10
B	1	3	1
C	1	3	3
D	1	10	10
E	3	1	10

8. The element of an electric kettle has a resistance of 30 Ω. The kettle is connected to a mains supply. The r.m.s. voltage of this supply is 230 V. The peak value of the current in the kettle is

A   0·13 A

B   0·18 A

C   5·4 A

D   7·7 A

E   10·8 A.

9. Four resistors, each of resistance 20 Ω, are connected to a 60 V supply of negligible internal resistance, as shown.

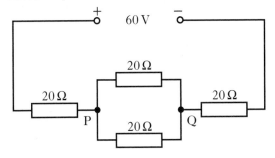

The potential difference across PQ is

A   12 V

B   15 V

C   20 V

D   24 V

E   30 V.

10. A signal from a power supply is displayed on an oscilloscope.

The trace on the oscilloscope is shown.

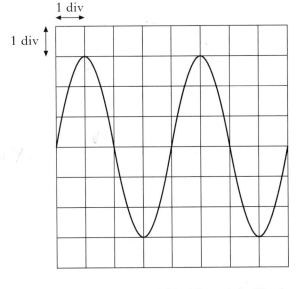

The time-base is set at 0·01 s/div and the Y-gain is set at 4·0 V/div.

Which row in the table shows the r.m.s. voltage and the frequency of the signal?

	r.m.s. voltage/V	frequency/Hz
A	8·5	25
B	12	25
C	24	25
D	8·5	50
E	12	50

11. A resistor and an ammeter are connected to a signal generator which has an output of constant amplitude and variable frequency.

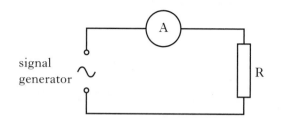

Which graph shows the relationship between the current I in the resistor and the output frequency f of the signal generator?

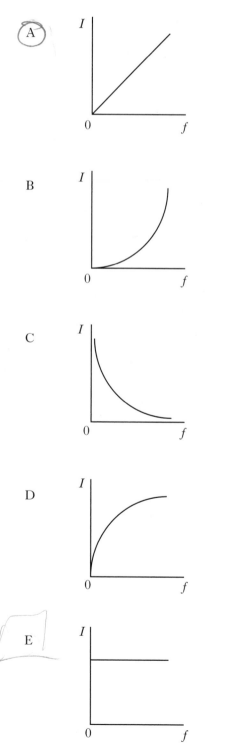

12. An oscilloscope is used to measure the frequency of the output voltage from an op-amp.

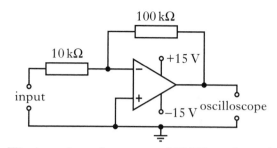

The input has a frequency of 280 Hz and a peak voltage of 0·5 V.

The frequency of the output voltage is

A   28 Hz

B   140 Hz

C   280 Hz

D   560 Hz

E   2800 Hz .

F: 280Hz

(constant)

13. An op-amp circuit is set up as shown.

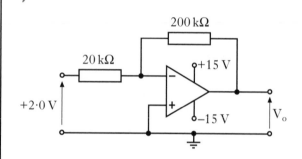

A voltage of +2·0 V is applied to the input. The voltage output, V_o, is approximately

A   +20 V

B   +15 V

C   −2·0 V

D   −15 V

E   −20 V.

$N_o = N_I$

$\dfrac{N_o}{N_I} = \dfrac{R_F}{R_I}$

$\dfrac{N_o}{2} = -\dfrac{200}{20}$

$\dfrac{N_o}{2} = 10$

$N = -20$

14. The energy of a wave depends on its

   A amplitude

   B period

   C phase

   D speed

   E wavelength.

15. A ray of light travels from air into a glass prism. The refractive index of the glass is 1·50.

Which diagram shows the correct path of the ray?

$n = \dfrac{\sin \theta_1}{\sin \theta_2}$

$1.50 =$

A
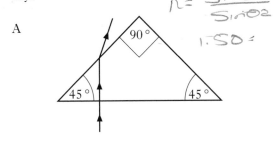

B
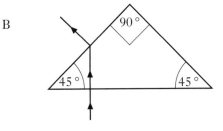

C
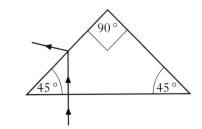

D
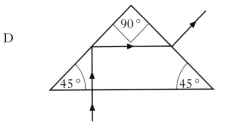

E
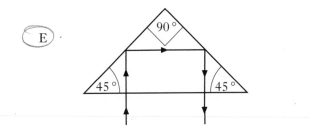

16. A beam of white light is passed through two optical components P and Q. Component P produces a number of spectra and component Q produces a spectrum as shown.

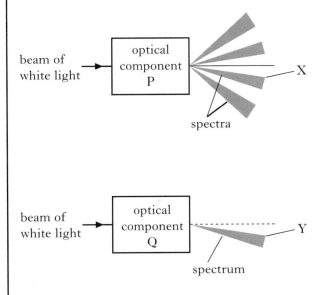

Which row in the table identifies the optical components and the colour of light seen at position X and position Y?

	Optical component P	Colour seen at X	Optical component Q	Colour seen at Y
A	grating	red	triangular prism	red
B	grating	red	triangular prism	violet
C	grating	violet	triangular prism	red
D	triangular prism	red	grating	violet
E	triangular prism	violet	grating	red

[Turn over

17. The diagram represents some electron transitions between energy levels in an atom.

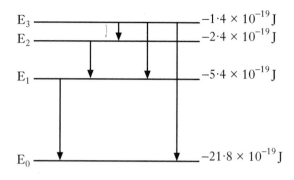

E_3 ——————— $-1\cdot4 \times 10^{-19}$ J
E_2 ——————— $-2\cdot4 \times 10^{-19}$ J

E_1 ——————— $-5\cdot4 \times 10^{-19}$ J

E_0 ——————— $-21\cdot8 \times 10^{-19}$ J

The radiation emitted with the shortest wavelength is produced by an electron making transition

A E_1 to E_0

B E_2 to E_1

C E_3 to E_2

D E_3 to E_1

E E_3 to E_0.

18. In the following circuit, component X is used to drive a motor.

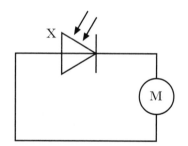

Which of the following gives the name of component X and its mode of operation?

	Name of component X	Mode of operation
A	light-emitting diode	photoconductive
B	light-emitting diode	photovoltaic
C	photodiode	photoconductive
D	photodiode	photovoltaic
E	op-amp	inverting

19. The classical experiment on the scattering of alpha particles from a thin gold foil suggested that

A   positive charges were evenly distributed throughout the atom

B   atomic nuclei were very small and positively charged

C   neutrons existed in the nucleus

D   alpha particles were helium nuclei

E   alpha particles were hydrogen nuclei.

20. A radioactive source produces a count rate of 2400 counts per second in a detector. When a lead plate of thickness 36 mm is placed between the source and the detector the count rate falls to 300 counts per second.

The half-value thickness of lead for this radiation is

A   4·5 mm

B   12 mm

C   36 mm

D   108 mm

E   288 mm.

[Turn over for SECTION B on *Page ten*

⑦

SECTION B

Write your answers to questions 21 to 31 in the answer book.

Marks

MEC **21.** Competitors are racing remote control cars. The cars have to be driven over a precise route between checkpoints.

Checkpoint A

Each car is to travel from checkpoint A to checkpoint B by following these instructions.

"Drive 150 m due North, then drive 250 m on a bearing of 60° East of North (060)."

Car X takes 1 minute 6 seconds to follow these instructions exactly.

(a) By scale drawing or otherwise, find the displacement of checkpoint B from checkpoint A. ②

(b) Calculate the average velocity of car X from checkpoint A to checkpoint B. ②

(c) Car Y leaves A at the same time as car X.

Car Y follows exactly the same route at an average speed of 6·5 m s⁻¹.

Which car arrives first at checkpoint B?

Justify your answer with a calculation. ②

(d) State the displacement of checkpoint A from checkpoint B. ①

(7)

[handwritten working]

a) 350m bearing 038°

$V = \frac{s}{t} = \frac{350}{6.6}$ 53.84 ms⁻¹ bearing 0.38°   5.3 ms⁻¹

y= 6.5ms⁻¹

V = d/t

t = d/v

t = 350/6.5

= 53.8s

400/6.5 = 61.5

x = d/v = 350/5.3

∴ y

d) 238°

Marks

MEC **22.** A fairground ride consists of rafts which slide down a slope into water.

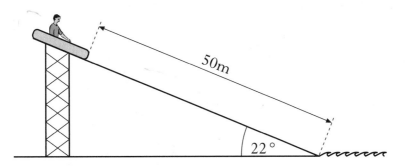

The slope is at an angle of 22° to the horizontal. Each raft has a mass of 8·0 kg. The length of the slope is 50 m.

A child of mass 52 kg sits in a raft at the top of the slope. The raft is released from rest. The child and raft slide together down the slope into the water. The force of friction between the raft and slope remains constant at 180 N.

(a) Calculate the component of weight, in newtons, of the child and raft down the slope.   ①

(b) Show by calculation that the acceleration of the child and raft down the slope is 0·67 m s^{-2}.   ②

(c) Calculate the speed of the child and raft at the bottom of the slope.   ②

(d) A second child of smaller mass is released from rest in an identical raft at the same starting point. The force of friction is the same as before.

How does the speed of this child and raft at the bottom of the slope compare with the answer to part (c)?

Justify your answer.   ②

(7)

[Turn over

a) Component of weight = mgSinθ
60 × 9.8 × Sin 22
= 220.27 N

b) F = ma
a = F/m = (220.27 - 180)/60
= 0.67 ms^{-2}

c) v = d/t.
v^2 = u^2 + 2as
v^2 = 0 + 2 × 0.67 × 50
v^2 = 67
v = 8.18 ms^{-1}

d) Smaller mass will have a higher velocity as less component force. (higher acceleration)

Marks

ME C **23.** A rigid cylinder contains $8.0 \times 10^{-2} \, m^3$ of helium gas at a pressure of 750 kPa. Gas is released from the cylinder to fill party balloons.

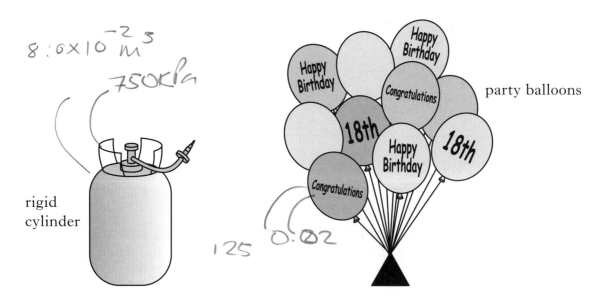

$8.0 \times 10^{-2} m^3$

$750 KPa$

rigid
cylinder

party balloons

125 0.02

During the filling process, the temperature remains constant. When filled, each balloon holds $0.020 \, m^3$ of helium gas at a pressure of 125 kPa.

(a) Calculate the total volume of the helium gas when it is at a pressure of 125 kPa.   2

(b) Determine the maximum number of balloons which can be fully inflated by releasing gas from the cylinder.   2

(c) State how the density of the helium gas in an inflated balloon compares to the initial density of the helium gas inside the cylinder.

Justify your answer.   2

(6)

a) $P_1 V_1 = P_2 V_2$

$750 \times 8.0 \times 10^{-2} = 125 V$

$V = \dfrac{8 \times 10^{-2} \times 125}{750}$

$= 0.48 \, m^3$

b) $0.48 - 0.08 = 40$

$\dfrac{0.40}{0.02} = 20$ balloons.

c) less dense in balloon.
$\checkmark \checkmark$ $P \downarrow$

Marks

24. The apparatus shown in the diagram is designed to accelerate alpha particles.

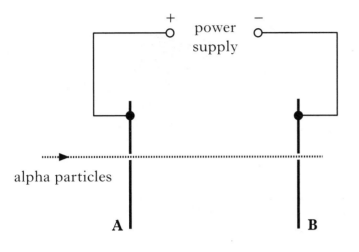

An alpha particle travelling at a speed of $2 \cdot 60 \times 10^6 \, \text{m s}^{-1}$ passes through a hole in plate A. The mass of an alpha particle is $6 \cdot 64 \times 10^{-27} \, \text{kg}$ and its charge is $3 \cdot 2 \times 10^{-19} \, \text{C}$.

(a) When the alpha particle reaches plate B, its kinetic energy has increased to $3 \cdot 05 \times 10^{-14} \, \text{J}$.

Show that the work done on the alpha particle as it moves from plate A to plate B is $8 \cdot 1 \times 10^{-15} \, \text{J}$.

2

(b) Calculate the potential difference between plates A and B.

2

(c) The apparatus is now adapted to accelerate **electrons** from A to B through the same potential difference.

How does the increase in the kinetic energy of an electron compare with the increase in kinetic energy of the alpha particle in part (a)?

Justify your answer.

2

(6)

$E_k = \frac{1}{2} m v^2$

$= \frac{1}{2} \, 6.64 \times 10^{-27} \, (2.6 \times 10^6)^2$

$\therefore \quad 2.2.44 \times 10^{+4} \quad]$

$3.05 \times 10^{-15} - 2.2 \times 4 \times 10^{-14}$

$= 8.1 \times 10^{-15} \, J.$

b) $PD = IR$
$= 2.53 \times 10^4 V$

$W = QV$

$V = W/Q$

$= \dfrac{8.1 \times 10^{-15}}{3.2 \times 10^{-19}}$

$= 2.53 \times 10^{-27}$

c) ?

[Turn over

Marks

25. A power supply of e.m.f. E and internal resistance $2 \cdot 0\,\Omega$ is connected as shown.

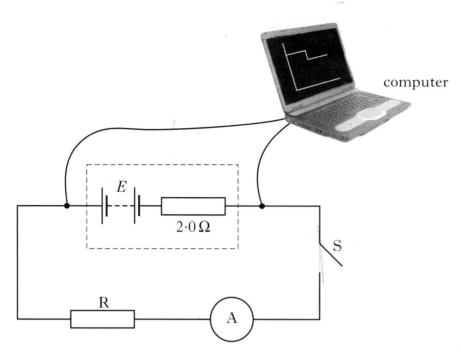

The computer connected to the apparatus displays a graph of potential difference against time.

The graph shows the potential difference across the terminals of the power supply for a short time before and after switch S is closed.

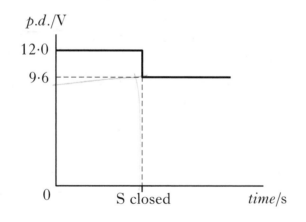

(a) State the e.m.f. of the power supply. ⟶ .12√   ①

(b) Calculate:

    (i) the reading on the ammeter after switch S is closed;   ②

    (ii) the resistance of resistor R.   ①

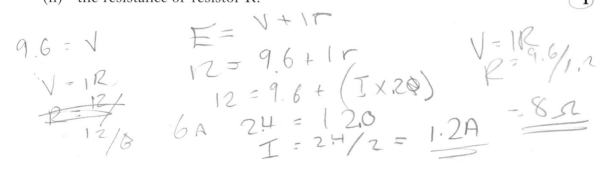

Marks

25.   (continued)

(*c*)   Switch S is opened. A second identical resistor is now connected in parallel
with R as shown.

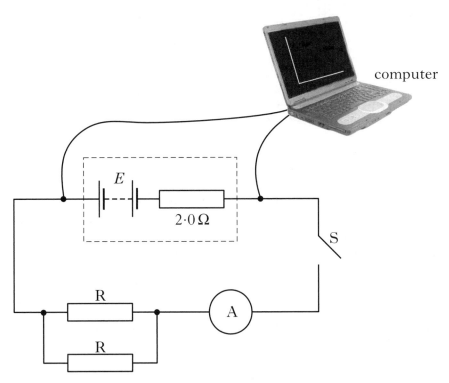

The computer is again connected in order to display a graph of potential
difference against time.

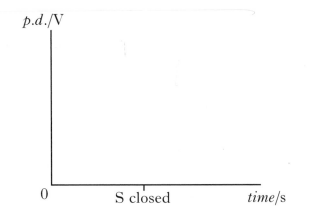

Copy and complete the new graph of potential difference against time
showing the values of potential difference before and after switch S is
closed.

2

(6)

[Turn over

Marks

26. An uncharged $2200\,\mu F$ capacitor is connected in a circuit as shown.

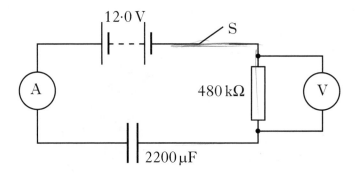

12·0 V

S

A

480 kΩ

V

2200 μF

The battery has negligible internal resistance.

(a) Switch S is closed. Calculate the initial charging current.

2

(b) At one instant during the charging process the potential difference **across the resistor** is 3·8 V.

Calculate the charge stored in the capacitor at this instant.

3

(c) Calculate the **maximum** energy the capacitor stores in this circuit.

2

(7)

$$C = 2200\mu F$$

$$V = 1L$$

$$R = 480,000\,\Omega$$

$$V = IR$$
$$I = V/R = \quad 12/480,000$$
$$= 2.5\times10^{-5}\,A$$

b) $\quad Q = CV$.
$$Q = (2200\times10^{-3}) \times 8.82$$
$$= \cancel{15.36} \quad 1.8\times10^{-2}\,C$$

c) $\quad E = \tfrac{1}{2}QV^2$
$$E = \tfrac{1}{2}(1.8\times10^{-2})\,12^2$$
$$= 1.296\times10^{-4}\,J$$

Marks

27. A Wheatstone bridge is used to measure the resistance of a thermistor as its temperature changes.

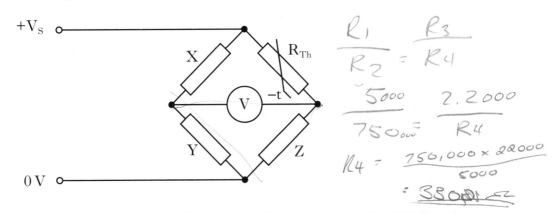

$$\frac{R_1}{R_2} = \frac{R_3}{R_4}$$

$$\frac{5000}{7500} = \frac{2.2000}{R_4}$$

$$R_4 = \frac{750,000 \times 22000}{5000}$$

$$= 3300 \ \Omega$$

(a) The bridge is balanced when X = 2·2 kΩ, Y = 5·0 kΩ and Z = 750 Ω.

   Calculate the resistance of the thermistor, R_{Th}, when the bridge is balanced.   2

(b) A student uses this bridge in a circuit to light an LED when the temperature in a greenhouse falls below a certain level.

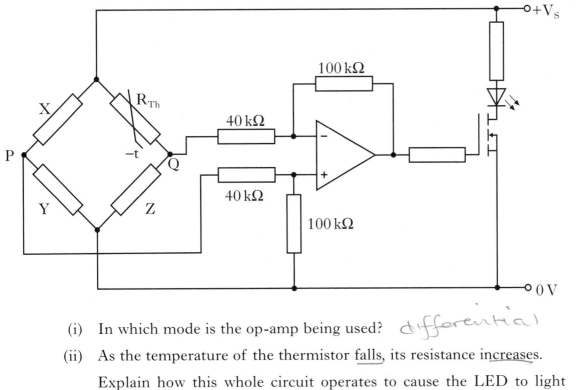

   (i) In which mode is the op-amp being used? differential   1

   (ii) As the temperature of the thermistor falls, its resistance increases.

   Explain how this whole circuit operates to cause the LED to light when the temperature falls.   2

   (iii) At a certain temperature the output voltage of the op-amp is 3·0 V.

   Calculate the potential difference between P and Q at this temperature.   2

(7)

R ↑, loss light εκ.

$$V_o = \frac{Rf}{R1}(V_2 - V_1)$$

$$3 = \frac{100}{40} \times (V)$$

$$V = \frac{3}{2.5} = 1.2 \ V$$

[Turn over

Marks

28. An experiment to determine the wavelength of light from a laser is shown.

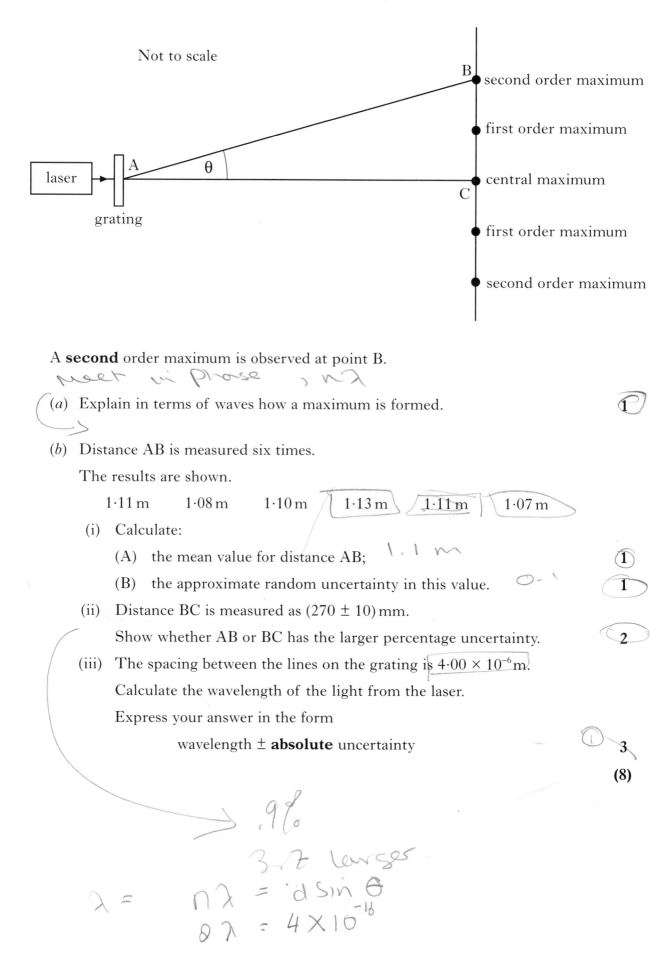

A **second** order maximum is observed at point B.

meet in Phase , n λ

(a) Explain in terms of waves how a maximum is formed. ①

(b) Distance AB is measured six times.

The results are shown.

1·11 m   1·08 m   1·10 m   1·13 m   1·11 m   1·07 m

(i) Calculate:

(A) the mean value for distance AB;   *1·1 m* ①

(B) the approximate random uncertainty in this value.   *0·1* ①

(ii) Distance BC is measured as (270 ± 10) mm.

Show whether AB or BC has the larger percentage uncertainty. ②

(iii) The spacing between the lines on the grating is 4·00 × 10⁻⁶ m.

Calculate the wavelength of the light from the laser.

Express your answer in the form

wavelength ± **absolute** uncertainty ① 3

(8)

.9%

3.7 lenses

$$\lambda = \qquad n\lambda = d \sin \theta$$
$$2\lambda = 4 \times 10^{-16}$$

Marks

29. A ray of red light is incident on a semicircular block of glass at the mid point of XY as shown.

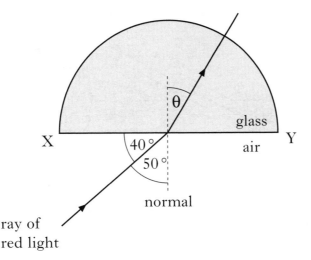

The refractive index of the block is 1·50 for this red light.

(a) Calculate angle θ shown on the diagram.   2

(b) The wavelength of the red light **in the glass** is 420 nm.

Calculate the wavelength of the light in air.   2

(c) The ray of red light is replaced by a ray of blue light incident at the same angle. The blue light enters the block at the same point.

Explain why the path taken by the blue light in the block is different to that taken by the red light.   1

                                                                                      (5)

[Turn over

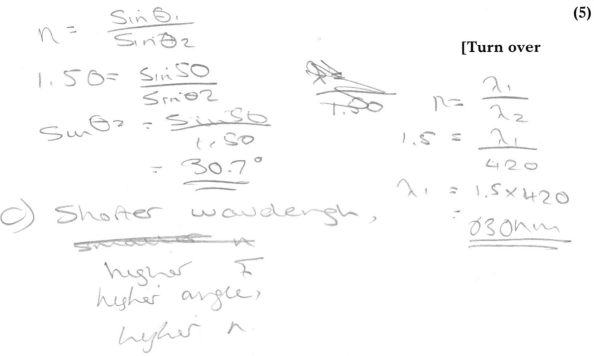

$$n = \frac{\sin \theta_1}{\sin \theta_2}$$

$$1.50 = \frac{\sin 50}{\sin \theta_2}$$

$$\sin \theta_2 = \frac{\sin 50}{1.50}$$

$$= 30.7°$$

c) Shorter wavelength,

higher f
higher angle,
higher n

$$n = \frac{\lambda_1}{\lambda_2}$$

$$1.5 = \frac{\lambda_1}{420}$$

$$\lambda_1 = 1.5 \times 420$$

$$= 630\text{nm}$$

④

Marks

30. A metal plate emits electrons when certain wavelengths of electromagnetic radiation are incident on it.

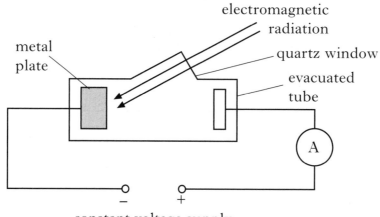

When light of wavelength 605 nm is incident on the metal plate, electrons are released with zero kinetic energy.

(a) Show that the work function of this metal is $3 \cdot 29 \times 10^{-19}$ J.   2

(b) The wavelength of the incident radiation is now altered. Photons of energy $5 \cdot 12 \times 10^{-19}$ J are incident on the metal plate.

   (i) Calculate the maximum kinetic energy of the electrons just as they leave the metal plate.   1

   (ii) The irradiance of this radiation on the metal plate is now decreased.

   State the effect this has on the ammeter reading.

   Justify your answer.   2

   (5)

$W = fg$

$= h f_0 .$

$\dfrac{V}{\lambda} = \dfrac{3 \times 10^8}{605 \times 10^{-9}}$

$= 4 \cdot 96 \times 10^{14}$

$= 6 \cdot 63 \times 10^{-34} \times 4 \cdot 96 \times 10^{14}$

$= 3 \cdot 29 \times 10^{-19}$ J

$5 \cdot 12 \times 10^{-19} \times 3 \cdot 29 \times 10^{-19}$

$= 1 \cdot 83 \times 10^{-19}$ Hz

b i) $E_K = \frac{1}{2} m v^2$

$E_K = hf - hf_0$

$= 6 \cdot 63 \times 10^{-34} \times$

ii) less A

Marks

31. (*a*) The following statement represents a nuclear reaction.

$$^{240}_{94}\text{Pu} \longrightarrow {}^{236}_{92}\text{U} + {}^{4}_{2}\text{He}$$

The table shows the masses of the particles involved in this reaction.

Particle	Mass/kg
$^{240}_{94}\text{Pu}$	$398{\cdot}626 \times 10^{-27}$
$^{236}_{92}\text{U}$	$391{\cdot}970 \times 10^{-27}$
$^{4}_{2}\text{He}$	$6{\cdot}645 \times 10^{-27}$

Calculate the energy released in this reaction.

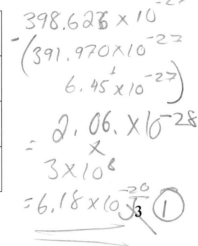

(*b*) A technician is working with a radioactive source as shown.

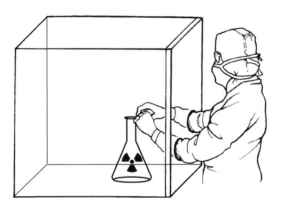

The technician's hands receive an absorbed dose at a rate of $4{\cdot}0\,\mu\text{Gy h}^{-1}$ for 2 hours. The radiation from the source has a radiation weighting factor of 3. Calculate the equivalent dose received by the technician's hands.

3

(6)

[END OF QUESTION PAPER]

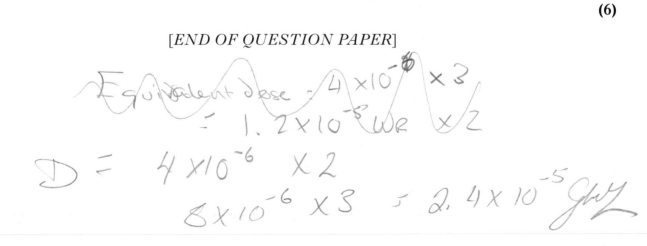

[BLANK PAGE]

HIGHER

2008

[BLANK PAGE]

X069/301

NATIONAL
QUALIFICATIONS
2008

FRIDAY, 23 MAY
1.00 PM – 3.30 PM

PHYSICS
HIGHER

Read Carefully

Reference may be made to the Physics Data Booklet.

1   All questions should be attempted.

Section A (questions 1 to 20)

2   Check that the answer sheet is for Physics Higher (Section A).

3   For this section of the examination you must use an **HB pencil** and, where necessary, an eraser.

4   Check that the answer sheet you have been given has **your name**, **date of birth**, **SCN** (Scottish Candidate Number) and **Centre Name** printed on it.

     Do not change any of these details.

5   If any of this information is wrong, tell the Invigilator immediately.

6   If this information is correct, **print** your name and seat number in the boxes provided.

7   There is **only one correct** answer to each question.

8   Any rough working should be done on the question paper or the rough working sheet, **not** on your answer sheet.

9   At the end of the exam, put the **answer sheet for Section A inside the front cover of your answer book**.

10   Instructions as to how to record your answers to questions 1–20 are given on page three.

Section B (questions 21 to 30)

11   Answer the questions numbered 21 to 30 in the answer book provided.

12   **All answers must be written clearly and legibly in ink**.

13   Fill in the details on the front of the answer book.

14   Enter the question number clearly in the margin of the answer book beside each of your answers to questions 21 to 30.

15   Care should be taken to give an appropriate number of significant figures in the final answers to calculations.

16   Where additional paper, eg square ruled paper, is used, write your name and SCN (Scottish Candidate Number) on it and place it inside the front cover of your answer booklet.

DATA SHEET
COMMON PHYSICAL QUANTITIES

Quantity	Symbol	Value	Quantity	Symbol	Value
Speed of light in vacuum	c	3.00×10^8 m s^{-1}	Mass of electron	m_e	9.11×10^{-31} kg
Magnitude of the charge on an electron	e	1.60×10^{-19} C	Mass of neutron	m_n	1.675×10^{-27} kg
Gravitational acceleration on Earth	g	9.8 m s^{-2}	Mass of proton	m_p	1.673×10^{-27} kg
Planck's constant	h	6.63×10^{-34} J s			

REFRACTIVE INDICES
The refractive indices refer to sodium light of wavelength 589 nm and to substances at a temperature of 273 K.

Substance	Refractive index	Substance	Refractive index
Diamond	2.42	Water	1.33
Crown glass	1.50	Air	1.00

SPECTRAL LINES

Element	Wavelength/nm	Colour	Element	Wavelength/nm	Colour
Hydrogen	656	Red	Cadmium	644	Red
	486	Blue-green		509	Green
	434	Blue-violet		480	Blue
	410	Violet		Lasers	
	397	Ultraviolet	Element	Wavelength/nm	Colour
	389	Ultraviolet	Carbon dioxide	9550 10590	Infrared
Sodium	589	Yellow	Helium-neon	633	Red

PROPERTIES OF SELECTED MATERIALS

Substance	Density/ kg m^{-3}	Melting Point/ K	Boiling Point/ K
Aluminium	2.70×10^3	933	2623
Copper	8.96×10^3	1357	2853
Ice	9.20×10^2	273	. . . .
Sea Water	1.02×10^3	264	377
Water	1.00×10^3	273	373
Air	1.29	. . . .	. . . .
Hydrogen	9.0×10^{-2}	14	20

The gas densities refer to a temperature of 273 K and a pressure of 1.01×10^5 Pa.

SECTION A

For questions 1 to 20 in this section of the paper the answer to each question is either A, B, C, D or E. Decide what your answer is, then, using your pencil, put a horizontal line in the space provided—see the example below.

EXAMPLE

The energy unit measured by the electricity meter in your home is the

    A kilowatt-hour

    B ampere

    C watt

    D coulomb

    E volt.

The correct answer is **A**—kilowatt-hour. The answer **A** has been clearly marked in **pencil** with a horizontal line (see below).

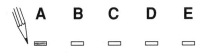

Changing an answer

If you decide to change your answer, carefully erase your first answer and, using your pencil, fill in the answer you want. The answer below has been changed to **E**.

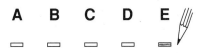

[Turn over

SECTION A

Answer questions 1–20 on the answer sheet.

1. Which row in the table is correct?

	Scalar	*Vector*
A	distance	work
B	weight	acceleration
C	velocity	displacement
D	mass	momentum
E	speed	time

2. A javelin is thrown at 60° to the horizontal with a speed of $20\ \mathrm{m\,s^{-1}}$.

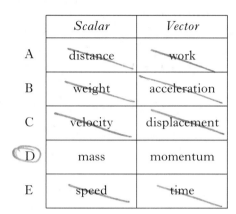

The javelin is in flight for 3·5 s.
Air resistance is negligible.
The horizontal distance the javelin travels is

A   35·0 m
B   60·6 m
C   70·0 m
D   121 m
E   140 m.

$20\ \cos\ 60$
$= 10m$
$d = vt$
$= 35m$

3. Two boxes on a frictionless horizontal surface are joined together by a string. A constant horizontal force of 12 N is applied as shown.

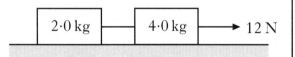

The tension in the string joining the two boxes is

A   2·0 N
B   4·0 N
C   6·0 N
D   8·0 N
E   12 N.

$2F = 4+12 = 8612$
$2F + 48 = 72$
$F = 72-48$
$F = 24/2$
$= 12$

4. The total mass of a motorcycle and rider is 250 kg. During braking, they are brought to rest from a speed of $16\!\cdot\!0\ \mathrm{m\,s^{-1}}$ in a time of $10\!\cdot\!0\ \mathrm{s}$.

The maximum energy which could be converted to heat in the brakes is

A   2000 J
B   4000 J
C   32 000 J
D   40 000 J
E   64 000 J.

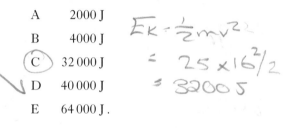
$E_K = \frac{1}{2}mv^2$
$= 25 \times 16^2/2$
$= 3200\ J$

5. A shell of mass 5·0 kg is travelling horizontally with a speed of $200\ \mathrm{m\,s^{-1}}$. It explodes into two parts. One part of mass 3·0 kg continues in the original direction with a speed of $100\ \mathrm{m\,s^{-1}}$.

The other part also continues in this same direction. Its speed is

A $150\ \mathrm{m\,s^{-1}}$
B $200\ \mathrm{m\,s^{-1}}$
C $300\ \mathrm{m\,s^{-1}}$
D $350\ \mathrm{m\,s^{-1}}$
E $700\ \mathrm{m\,s^{-1}}$.

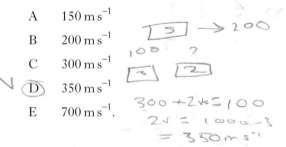
$300 + 2 \times 5100$
$2v = 1000-3$
$= 350\ m s^{-1}$

6. The graph shows the force which acts on an object over a time interval of 8 seconds.

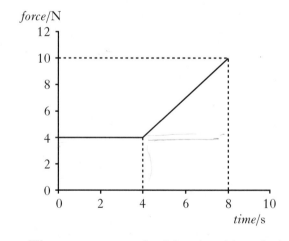

The momentum gained by the object during this 8 seconds is

A $12\ \mathrm{kg\,m\,s^{-1}}$
B $32\ \mathrm{kg\,m\,s^{-1}}$
C $44\ \mathrm{kg\,m\,s^{-1}}$
D $52\ \mathrm{kg\,m\,s^{-1}}$
E $72\ \mathrm{kg\,m\,s^{-1}}$.

7. One pascal is equivalent to

   A   1 N m

   B   1 N m^2

   C   1 N m^3

   D   1 N m^{-2}

   E   1 N m^{-3}.

8. An electron is accelerated from rest through a potential difference of 2·0 kV.

   The kinetic energy gained by the electron is

   A   8·0 × 10^{-23} J

   B   8·0 × 10^{-20} J

   C   3·2 × 10^{-19} J

   D   1·6 × 10^{-16} J

   E   3·2 × 10^{-16} J.

   $E = \frac{1}{2}QV$
   $= 1.6 \times 10^{-19} \times 2$

9. The e.m.f. of a battery is

   A   the total energy supplied by the battery

   B   the voltage lost due to the internal resistance of the battery

   C   the total charge which passes through the battery

   D   the number of coulombs of charge passing through the battery per second

   E   the energy supplied to each coulomb of charge passing through the battery.

10. The diagram shows the trace on an oscilloscope when an alternating voltage is applied to its input.

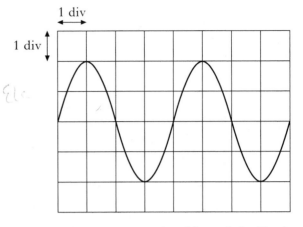

The timebase is set at 5 ms/div and the Y-gain is set at 10 V/div.

Which row in the table gives the peak voltage and the frequency of the signal?

	Peak voltage/V	Frequency/Hz
A	7·1	20
B	14	50
C	20	20
D	20	50
E	40	50

Peak Voltage

= 10 × 2 = 20

Frequency = $\frac{1}{period}$.

10 × 5

= 50

[Turn over

11. A resistor is connected to an a.c. supply as shown.

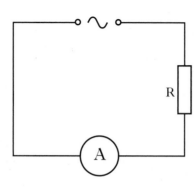

a.c. ammeter

The supply has a constant peak voltage, but its frequency can be varied.

The frequency is steadily increased from 50 Hz to 5000 Hz.

The reading on the a.c. ammeter

A   remains constant

B   decreases steadily

C   increases steadily

D   increases then decreases

E   decreases then increases.

12. An ideal op-amp is connected as shown.

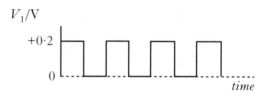

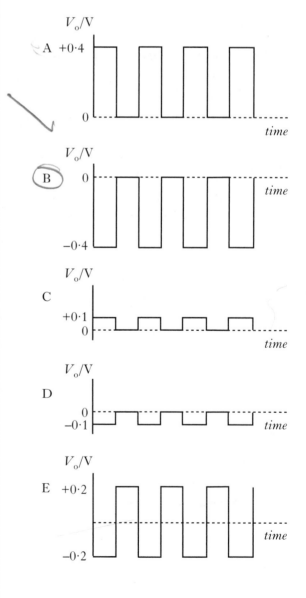

The graph shows how the input voltage, V_1, varies with time.

Which graph shows how the output voltage, V_o, varies with time?

13. Which of the following proves that light is transmitted as waves?

  A   Light has a high velocity.

  B   Light can be reflected.

  C   Light irradiance reduces with distance.

  D   Light can be refracted.

  E   Light can produce interference patterns.

14. A source of microwaves of wavelength λ is placed behind two slits, R and S.

A microwave detector records a maximum when it is placed at P.

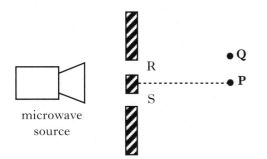

microwave source

The detector is moved and the **next** maximum is recorded at Q.

The path difference (SQ – RQ) is

  A   0

  B $\dfrac{\lambda}{2}$

  C λ

  D $\dfrac{3\lambda}{2}$

  E 2λ.

15. A student makes five separate measurements of the diameter of a lens.

These measurements are shown in the table.

Diameter of lens/mm	22·5	22·6	22·4	22·6	22·9

The approximate random uncertainty in the mean value of the diameter is

  A   0·1 mm

  B   0·2 mm

  C   0·3 mm

  D   0·4 mm

  E   0·5 mm.

$\bar{x} = 22.6$

$\dfrac{22.9 - 22.4}{5} = 0.1$

16. The value of the absolute refractive index of diamond is 2·42.

The critical angle for diamond is

  A   0·413°

  B   24·4°

  C   42·0°

  D   65·6°

  E   90·0°.

$\sin\theta c = \dfrac{1}{n}$

$= 24.4°$

[Turn over

17. Part of the energy level diagram for an atom is shown.

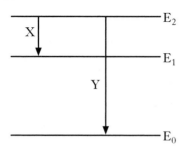

X and Y represent two possible electron transitions.
Which of the following statements is/are correct?

I   Transition Y produces photons of higher frequency than transition X.

II Transition X produces photons of longer wavelength than transition Y.

III When an electron is in the energy level E_0, the atom is ionised.

A   I only

B   I and II only

C   I and III only

D   II and III only

E   I, II and III

18. The letters **X**, **Y** and **Z** represent three missing words from the following passage.

Materials can be divided into three broad categories according to their electrical resistance.

.................**X**.......... *have a very high resistance.*

.................**Y**.......... *have a high resistance in their pure form but when small amounts of certain impurities are added, the resistance decreases.*

.................**Z**.......... *have a low resistance.*

Which row in the table shows the missing words?

	X	Y	Z
A	conductors	insulators	semi-conductors
B	semi-conductors	insulators	conductors
C	insulators	semi-conductors	conductors
D	conductors	semi-conductors	insulators
E	insulators	conductors	semi-conductors

19. Compared with a proton, an alpha particle has

A   twice the mass and twice the charge

B   twice the mass and the same charge

C   four times the mass and twice the charge

D   four times the mass and the same charge

E   twice the mass and four times the charge.

20. For the nuclear decay shown, which row of the table gives the correct values of x, y and z?

$$^{214}_{x}\text{Pb} \longrightarrow ^{y}_{83}\text{Bi} + ^{0}_{z}\text{e}$$

	x	y	z
A	85	214	2
B	84	214	1
C	83	210	4
D	82	214	−1
E	82	210	−1

[Turn over for SECTION B on *Page ten*

SECTION B

Write your answers to questions 21 to 30 in the answer book.

Marks

21. To test the braking system of cars, a test track is set up as shown.

Mec

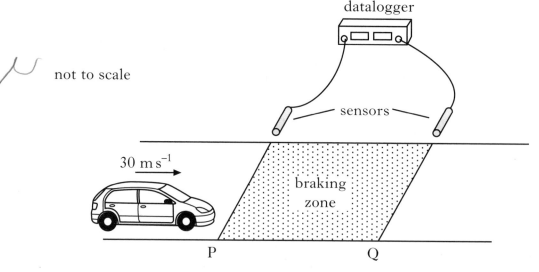

datalogger

not to scale

sensors

30 m s^{-1}

braking zone

P   Q

The sensors are connected to a datalogger which records the speed of a car at both P and Q.

A car is driven at a constant speed of 30 m s^{-1} until it reaches the start of the braking zone at P. The brakes are then applied.

(*a*) In one test, the datalogger records the speed at P as 30 m s^{-1} and the speed at Q as 12 m s^{-1}. The car slows down at a constant rate of $9 \cdot 0 \text{ m s}^{-2}$ between P and Q.

Calculate the length of the braking zone.   2

(*b*) The test is repeated. The same car is used but now with passengers in the car. The speed at P is again recorded as 30 m s^{-1}.

The same braking force is applied to the car as in part (*a*).

How does the speed of the car at Q compare with its speed at Q in part (*a*)? Justify your answer.   2

$v = 30 \text{ m s}^{-1}$

$u = 30 \text{ m s}^{-1}$

$v = 12 \text{ m s}^{-1}$

$a = -9.0 \text{ m s}^{-2}$

$d = ?$

$v^2 = u^2 + 2as$

$12^2 = 30^2 + (2 \times -9 \times s)$

$12^2 = 30^2 + -18 s$

$= 42 m$

b)

Marks

21. (continued)

(*c*)   The brake lights of the car consist of a number of very bright LEDs.

An LED from the brake lights is forward biased by connecting it to a 12 V car battery as shown.

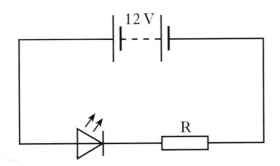

The battery has negligible internal resistance.

(i)   Explain, in terms of charge carriers, how the LED emits light.   1

(ii)   The LED is operating at its rated values of 5·0 V and 2·2 W.

Calculate the value of resistor R.   3

(8)

[Turn over

22. A crate of mass 40·0 kg is pulled up a slope using a rope.

The slope is at an angle of 30° to the horizontal.

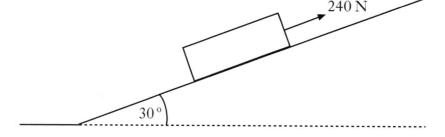

240 N

30°

A force of 240 N is applied to the crate parallel to the slope.

The crate moves at a constant speed of 3·0 m s⁻¹.

(a) (i)   Calculate the component of the weight of the crate acting parallel to
the slope. $mg\sin\theta = 40 \times 9.8 \times \sin 30 = 196N$ (2)

(ii) Calculate the frictional force acting on the crate.   (2)
$240 - 196 = -44N$

(b) As the crate is moving up the slope, the rope snaps.

The graph shows how the velocity of the crate changes from the moment
the rope snaps.

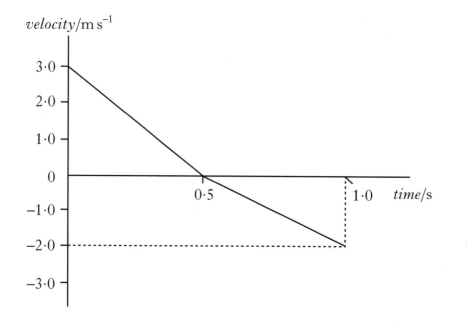

velocity/m s⁻¹

3·0

2·0

1·0

0

0·5   1·0   time/s

−1·0

−2·0

−3·0

(i)   Describe the motion of the crate during the first 0·5 s after the rope
snaps.   (1)

decelerating

Marks

22. (b) (continued)

Mec   (ii)   Copy the axes shown below and sketch the graph to show the acceleration of the crate between 0 and 1·0 s.

Appropriate numerical values are also required on the acceleration axis.

2

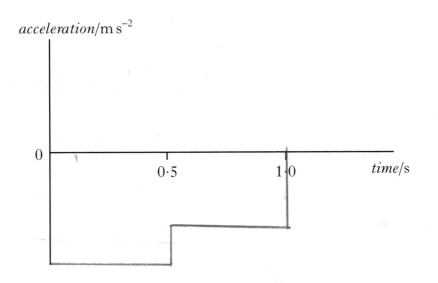

(iii)   Explain, in terms of the forces acting on the crate, why the magnitude of the acceleration changes at 0·5 s.

2

(9)

[Turn over

Marks

23.   A cylinder of compressed oxygen gas is in a laboratory.

(a) The oxygen inside the cylinder is at a pressure of $2 \cdot 82 \times 10^6$ Pa and a temperature of $19 \cdot 0\,°C$.

The cylinder is now moved to a storage room where the temperature is $5 \cdot 0\,°C$.

   (i) Calculate the pressure of the oxygen inside the cylinder when its temperature is $5 \cdot 0\,°C$.   **2**

   (ii) What effect, if any, does this decrease in temperature have on the density of the oxygen in the cylinder?

Justify your answer.   **2**

(b)   (i) The volume of oxygen inside the cylinder is $0 \cdot 030$ m^3.

The density of the oxygen inside the cylinder is $37 \cdot 6$ kg m^{-3}.

Calculate the mass of oxygen in the cylinder.   **2**

  (ii) The valve on the cylinder is opened slightly so that oxygen is gradually released.

The temperature of the oxygen inside the cylinder remains constant.

Explain, in terms of particles, why the pressure of the gas inside the cylinder decreases.   **1**

  (iii) After a period of time, the pressure of the oxygen inside the cylinder reaches a constant value of $1 \cdot 01 \times 10^5$ Pa. The valve remains open.

Explain why the pressure does not decrease below this value.   **1**

    (8)

i) $\dfrac{P_1}{T_1} = \dfrac{P_2}{T_2}$

$\dfrac{2.82 \times 10^6}{292} = \dfrac{P_2}{278}$

$P_2 = \dfrac{(2.82 \times 10^6) \times 278}{292}$

$= 2.68 \times 10^6\,Pa$ ✓

ii) less dense.
decrease in collisions + force.

b) i) $\rho = \frac{m}{V}$

$m = \rho V$
$= 0.03 \times 37.6$
$= 1.13\,kg$ ✓

ii) Pressure ↓,
molecules ↓
collisions ↓
Pressure ↓

iii) Pressure of air. ✓

Marks

24. Electrically heated gloves are used by skiers and climbers to provide extra warmth.

elc

(a) Each glove has a heating element of resistance 3·6 Ω.

Two cells, each of e.m.f. 1·5 V and internal resistance 0·20 Ω, are used to operate the heating element.

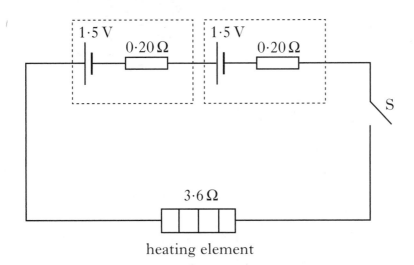

heating element

Switch S is closed.

(i) Determine the value of the total circuit resistance. $4\,\Omega$ ①

(ii) Calculate the current in the heating element. $0.4\,A$ ②

(iii) Calculate the power output of the heating element.   ②

(b) When in use, the internal resistance of each cell gradually increases.

What effect, if any, does this have on the power output of the heating element?

Justify your answer.   ① ②

(7)

Handwritten:

$3/4 = 0.75\,A$

$P = IV = 0.75 \times 1.5$

b) Decreases with higher R

iii) $I^2 R$
$0.75^2 \times 3.6$
$= 2.03\,W$

[Turn over

Marks

25. (*a*) State what is meant by the term *capacitance.* Amount of charge/electrical stored.   **1**

(*b*) An uncharged capacitor, C, is connected in a circuit as shown.

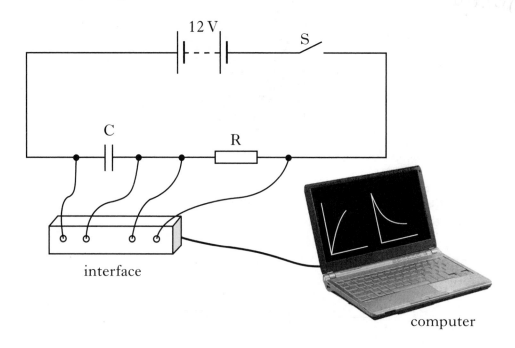

The 12 V battery has negligible internal resistance.

Switch S is closed and the capacitor begins to charge.

The interface measures the current in the circuit and the potential difference (p.d.) across the capacitor. These measurements are displayed as graphs on the computer.

Graph 1 shows the p.d. across the capacitor for the first 0·40 s of charging.

Graph 2 shows the current in the circuit for the first 0·40 s of charging.

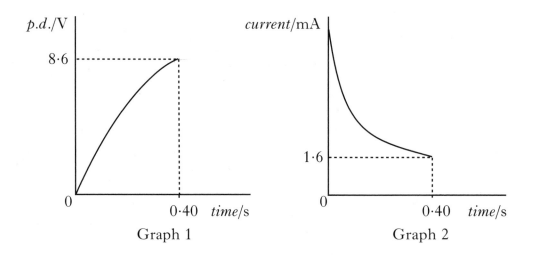

Marks

25. **(b)** **(continued)**

(i) Determine the p.d. **across resistor R** at 0·40 s. 8.6V   1

(ii) Calculate the resistance of R. $R = V/I = 8.6/1.6 = 5.4 \, \Omega$ 2

(iii) The capacitor takes 2·2 seconds to charge fully.

At that time it stores 10·8 mJ of energy.

Calculate the capacitance of the capacitor.

$C = Q/V \qquad E = \frac{1}{2}CV^2$

$10.8 = \frac{1}{2}C \times 8.6^2$

$10.8 = C \times 18.49$

$C = \dfrac{10.8 \times 10^{-3}}{18}$

$= 5.84 \times 10^{-4} \, C$

(c) The capacitor is now discharged.
A second, identical resistor is connected in the circuit as shown.

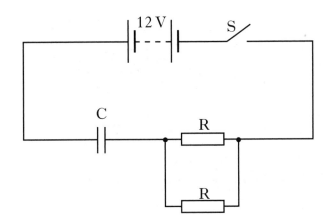

Switch S is closed.

Is the time taken for the capacitor to fully charge less than, equal to, or greater than the time taken to fully charge in part **(b)**?

Justify your answer.   2

(9)

[Turn over

Marks

26. The graph shows how the resistance of an LDR changes with the irradiance of light incident on it.

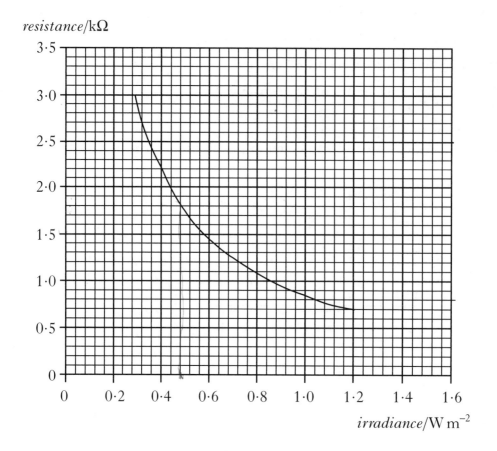

ue

(a) The LDR is connected in the following bridge circuit.

$V = IR$

$I = V/R$

$= 12/$

$R = IR$

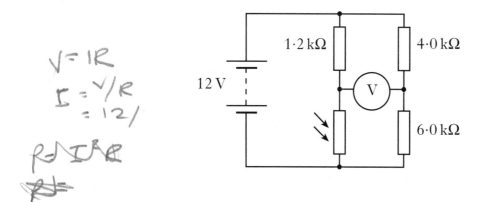

1·2 kΩ   4·0 kΩ

12 V

V

6·0 kΩ

Determine the value of irradiance at which the bridge is balanced.

Show clearly how you arrive at your answer.   3

$\dfrac{R_1}{R_2} = \dfrac{R_3}{R_4} = \dfrac{1.2}{R_2} = \dfrac{4}{6}$

$I = R/A$

$R_2 = \dfrac{1.2 \times 6}{4}$

$= 1.8 \text{ k}\Omega$

4.8 Wm^{-2}

$1.8 \text{ k}\Omega$

Marks

26. (continued)

(b) The LDR is now mounted on the outside of a car to monitor light level. It forms part of a circuit which provides an indication for the driver to switch on the headlamps.

The circuit is shown below.

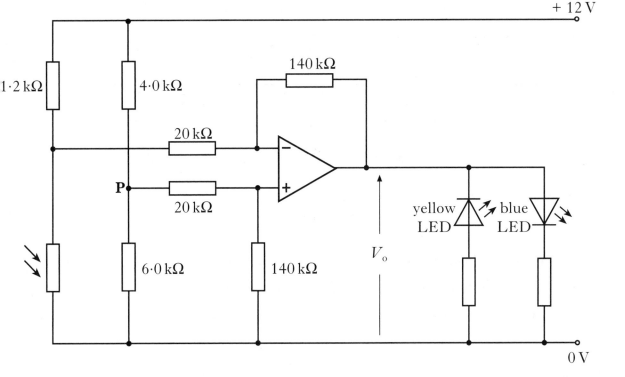

The LEDs inside the car indicate whether the headlamps should be on or off.

(i) At a particular value of irradiance the resistance of the LDR is $2 \cdot 0 \, k\Omega$.

Show that the potential difference across the LDR in the circuit is $7 \cdot 5 \, V$.   1

(ii) The potential at point P in the circuit is $7 \cdot 2 \, V$.

Calculate the output voltage, V_o, of the op-amp at this light level.   2

(iii) Which LED(s) is/are lit at this value of output voltage?

Justify your answer.   2

(8)

[Turn over

Marks

27. (a) A ray of red light of frequency $4 \cdot 80 \times 10^{14}$ Hz is incident on a glass lens as shown.

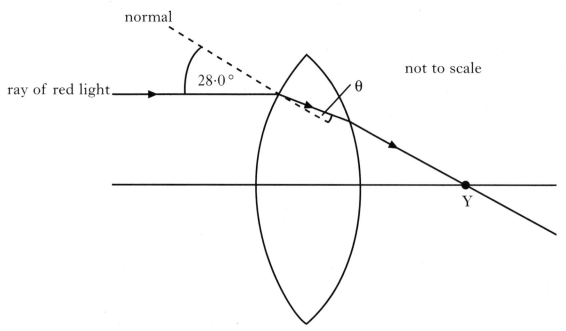

The ray passes through point Y after leaving the lens.

The refractive index of the glass is 1·61 for this red light.

(i) Calculate the value of the angle θ shown in the diagram.   2

(ii) Calculate the wavelength of this light inside the lens.   3

(b) The ray of red light is now replaced by a ray of blue light.

The ray is incident on the lens at the same point as in part (a).

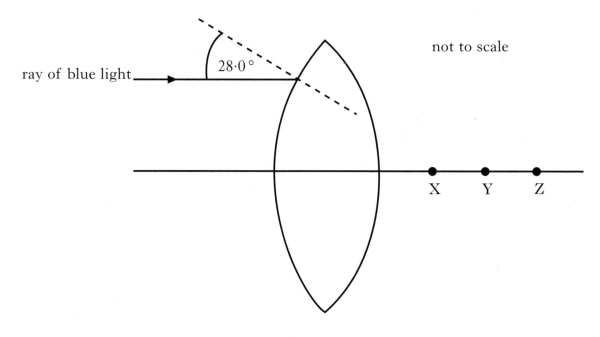

Through which point, X, Y or Z, will this ray pass after leaving the lens?

You must justify your answer.   1

(6)

Marks

28. The diagram shows a light sensor connected to a voltmeter.

A small lamp is placed in front of the sensor.

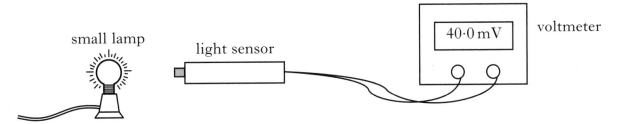

The reading on the voltmeter is 20 mV for each 1·0 mW of power incident on the sensor.

(*a*) The reading on the voltmeter is 40·0 mV.

The area of the light sensor is $8·0 \times 10^{-5}\,\text{m}^2$.

Calculate the irradiance of light on the sensor.   **3**

(*b*) The small lamp is replaced by a different source of light.

Using this new source, a student investigates how irradiance varies with distance.

The results are shown.

Distance/m	0·5	0·7	0·9
Irradiance/W m^{-2}	1·1	0·8	0·6

Can this new source be considered to be a point source of light?

Use **all** the data to justify your answer.   **2**

(5)

[Turn over

Marks

29. To explain the photoelectric effect, light can be considered as consisting of tiny bundles of energy. These bundles of energy are called photons.

(*a*) Sketch a graph to show the relationship between photon energy and frequency.

1

(*b*) Photons of frequency 6.1×10^{14} Hz are incident on the surface of a metal.

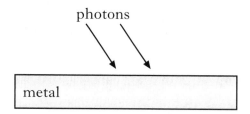

This releases photoelectrons from the surface of the metal.

The maximum kinetic energy of any of these photoelectrons is 6.0×10^{-20} J.

Calculate the work function of the metal.

3

(*c*) The irradiance due to these photons on the surface of the metal is now reduced.

Explain why the maximum kinetic energy of each photoelectron is unchanged.

1

(5)

Marks

30. (*a*) A technician is carrying out an experiment on the absorption of gamma radiation.

The radioactive source used has a long half-life and emits only gamma radiation. The activity of the source is 12 kBq.

   (i) State what is meant by an *activity of 12 kBq*.   **1**

  (ii) The table shows the half-value thicknesses of aluminium and lead for gamma radiation.

Material	Half-value thickness/mm
aluminium (Al)	60
lead (Pb)	15

The technician sets up the following apparatus.

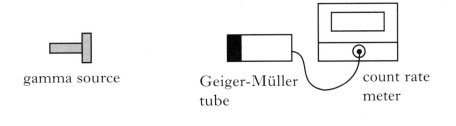

gamma source   Geiger-Müller   count rate
                                tube   meter

The count rate, when corrected for background radiation, is 800 counts per second.

Samples of aluminium and lead are now placed between the source and detector as shown.

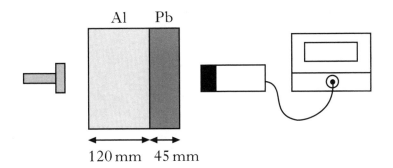

               Al   Pb

120 mm   45 mm

Determine the new corrected count rate.   **2**

[Turn over for Question 30 (*b*) on *Page twenty-four*

Marks

30. (continued)

(b) X-ray scanners are used as part of airport security. A beam of X-rays scans the luggage as it passes through the scanner.

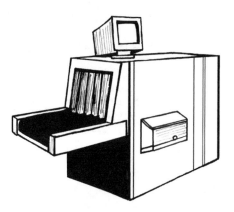

A baggage handler sometimes puts a hand inside the scanner to clear blockages.

The hand receives an average absorbed dose of 0·030 μGy each time this occurs.

The radiation weighting factor for X-rays is 1.

  (i) State the average equivalent dose received by the hand on each occasion.   1

  (ii) The occupational exposure limit for a hand is 60 μSv per hour.

      Calculate how many times the baggage handler would have to put a hand into the scanner in one hour to reach this limit.   1

                                                                                  (5)

[END OF QUESTION PAPER]

HIGHER

2009

[BLANK PAGE]

X069/301

NATIONAL
QUALIFICATIONS
2009

TUESDAY, 26 MAY
1.00 PM – 3.30 PM

PHYSICS
HIGHER

Read Carefully

Reference may be made to the Physics Data Booklet.

1 All questions should be attempted.

Section A (questions 1 to 20)

2 Check that the answer sheet is for Physics Higher (Section A).

3 For this section of the examination you must use an **HB pencil** and, where necessary, an eraser.

4 Check that the answer sheet you have been given has **your name**, **date of birth**, **SCN** (Scottish Candidate Number) and **Centre Name** printed on it.
  Do not change any of these details.

5 If any of this information is wrong, tell the Invigilator immediately.

6 If this information is correct, **print** your name and seat number in the boxes provided.

7 There is **only one correct** answer to each question.

8 Any rough working should be done on the question paper or the rough working sheet, **not** on your answer sheet.

9 At the end of the exam, put the **answer sheet for Section A inside the front cover of your answer book**.

10 Instructions as to how to record your answers to questions 1–20 are given on page three.

Section B (questions 21 to 30)

11 Answer the questions numbered 21 to 30 in the answer book provided.

12 **All answers must be written clearly and legibly in ink**.

13 Fill in the details on the front of the answer book.

14 Enter the question number clearly in the margin of the answer book beside each of your answers to questions 21 to 30.

15 Care should be taken to give an appropriate number of significant figures in the final answers to calculations.

16 Where additional paper, eg square ruled paper, is used, write your name and SCN (Scottish Candidate Number) on it and place it inside the front cover of your answer booklet.

DATA SHEET
COMMON PHYSICAL QUANTITIES

Quantity	Symbol	Value	Quantity	Symbol	Value
Speed of light in vacuum	c	3.00×10^8 m s^{-1}	Mass of electron	m_e	9.11×10^{-31} kg
Magnitude of the charge on an electron	e	1.60×10^{-19} C	Mass of neutron	m_n	1.675×10^{-27} kg
Gravitational acceleration on Earth	g	9.8 m s^{-2}	Mass of proton	m_p	1.673×10^{-27} kg
Planck's constant	h	6.63×10^{-34} J s			

REFRACTIVE INDICES
The refractive indices refer to sodium light of wavelength 589 nm and to substances at a temperature of 273 K.

Substance	Refractive index	Substance	Refractive index
Diamond	2·42	Water	1·33
Crown glass	1·50	Air	1·00

SPECTRAL LINES

Element	Wavelength/nm	Colour	Element	Wavelength/nm	Colour
Hydrogen	656	Red	Cadmium	644	Red
	486	Blue-green		509	Green
	434	Blue-violet		480	Blue
	410	Violet	Lasers		
	397	Ultraviolet	Element	Wavelength/nm	Colour
	389	Ultraviolet	Carbon dioxide	9550 } 10590 }	Infrared
Sodium	589	Yellow	Helium-neon	633	Red

PROPERTIES OF SELECTED MATERIALS

Substance	Density/ kg m^{-3}	Melting Point/ K	Boiling Point/ K
Aluminium	2.70×10^3	933	2623
Copper	8.96×10^3	1357	2853
Ice	9.20×10^2	273	. . . .
Sea Water	1.02×10^3	264	377
Water	1.00×10^3	273	373
Air	1·29	. . . .	. . . .
Hydrogen	9.0×10^{-2}	14	20

The gas densities refer to a temperature of 273 K and a pressure of 1.01×10^5 Pa.

SECTION A

For questions 1 to 20 in this section of the paper the answer to each question is either A, B, C, D or E. Decide what your answer is, then, using your pencil, put a horizontal line in the space provided—see the example below.

EXAMPLE

The energy unit measured by the electricity meter in your home is the

    A kilowatt-hour

    B ampere

    C watt

    D coulomb

    E volt.

The correct answer is **A**—kilowatt-hour. The answer **A** has been clearly marked in **pencil** with a horizontal line (see below).

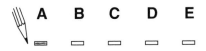

Changing an answer

If you decide to change your answer, carefully erase your first answer and, using your pencil, fill in the answer you want. The answer below has been changed to **E**.

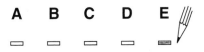

[Turn over

SECTION A

Answer questions 1–20 on the answer sheet.

Mec

1. Which of the following contains one vector and one scalar quantity?

   A   power; speed

   B   force; kinetic energy

   C   momentum; velocity

   D   work; potential energy

   E   displacement; acceleration

2. The following velocity-time graph represents the vertical motion of a ball.

Mec

Which of the following acceleration-time graphs represents the same motion?

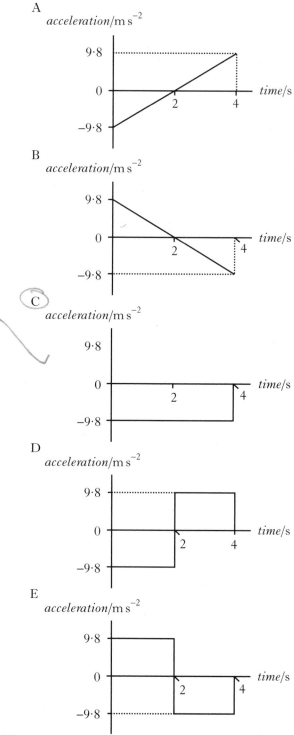

Page four

3. A box of weight 120 N is placed on a smooth horizontal surface.

A force of 20 N is applied to the box as shown.

Mec

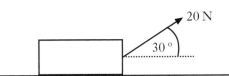

The box is pulled a distance of 50 m along the surface.

The work done in pulling the box is

A   500 J

B   866 J $Wd = Fd$

C   1000 J

D   6000 J

E   6866 J.

4. A skydiver of total mass 85 kg is falling vertically.

Mec

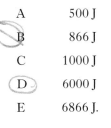

At one point during the fall, the air resistance on the skydiver is 135 N.

The acceleration of the skydiver at this point is

A $0 \cdot 6 \, \mathrm{m \, s^{-2}}$

B $1 \cdot 6 \, \mathrm{m \, s^{-2}}$

C $6 \cdot 2 \, \mathrm{m \, s^{-2}}$

D $8 \cdot 2 \, \mathrm{m \, s^{-2}}$

E $13 \cdot 8 \, \mathrm{m \, s^{-2}}$.

$M = 85 kg$ 9.8

$F = 735 N$ -1.6

$a =$

$F = ma$ $\dfrac{135}{85}$

$a = F/m =$

$= 1.6$

5. A 2·0 kg trolley travels in a straight line towards a stationary 5·0 kg trolley as shown.

Mec

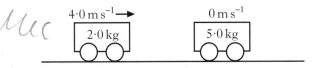

The trolleys collide. After the collision the trolleys move as shown below.

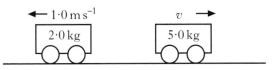

What is the speed v of the 5·0 kg trolley after the collision?

A $0 \cdot 4 \, \mathrm{m \, s^{-1}}$

B $1 \cdot 2 \, \mathrm{m \, s^{-1}}$

C $2 \cdot 0 \, \mathrm{m \, s^{-1}}$

D $2 \cdot 2 \, \mathrm{m \, s^{-1}}$

E $3 \cdot 0 \, \mathrm{m \, s^{-1}}$

6. The density of the gas in a container is initially $5 \cdot 0 \, \mathrm{kg \, m^{-3}}$.

Mec Which of the following increases the density of the gas?

I   Raising the temperature of the gas without changing its mass or volume.

II   Increasing the mass of the gas without changing its volume or temperature.

III   Increasing the volume of the gas without changing its mass or temperature.

A   II only

B   III only

C   I and II only

D   II and III only

E   I, II and III

$5/6$

[Turn over

7. For a fixed mass of gas at constant volume

Mac

   A   the pressure is directly proportional to temperature in °C

   B   the pressure is inversely proportional to temperature in °C

   C   the pressure is directly proportional to temperature in K

   D   the pressure is inversely proportional to temperature in K

   E   (pressure × temperature in K) is constant.

8. A potential difference, V, is applied between two metal plates. The plates are $0{\cdot}15\,\text{m}$ apart. A charge of $+4{\cdot}0\,\text{mC}$ is released from rest at the positively charged plate as shown.

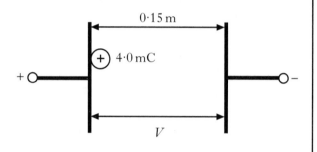

The kinetic energy of the charge just before it hits the negative plate is $8{\cdot}0\,\text{J}$.

The potential difference between the plates is

   A $3{\cdot}2 \times 10^{-2}\,\text{V}$

   B $1{\cdot}2\,\text{V}$

   C $2{\cdot}0\,\text{V}$

   D $2{\cdot}0 \times 10^{3}\,\text{V}$

   E $4{\cdot}0 \times 10^{3}\,\text{V}$.

Po. W/Q

9. A battery of e.m.f. 24 V and negligible internal resistance is connected as shown.

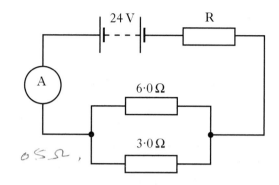

The reading on the ammeter is $2{\cdot}0\,\text{A}$.

The resistance of R is

   A $3{\cdot}0\,\Omega$

   B $4{\cdot}0\,\Omega$

   C $10\,\Omega$

   D $12\,\Omega$

   E $18\,\Omega$.

10. The diagram shows a Wheatstone Bridge.

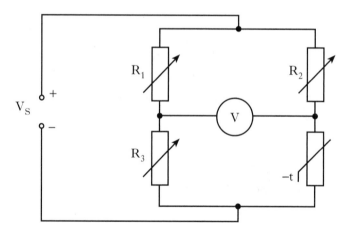

The bridge is initially balanced.

The thermistor is then heated and its resistance decreases. The bridge could be returned to balance by

   A   decreasing R_1

   B   decreasing R_2

   C   increasing R_2

   D   increasing R_3

   E   increasing V_S.

11. A 25·0 μF capacitor is charged until the potential difference across it is 500 V.

The charge stored in the capacitor is

A $5·00 \times 10^{-8}$ C

B $2·00 \times 10^{-5}$ C

C $1·25 \times 10^{-2}$ C

D $1·25 \times 10^{4}$ C

E $2·00 \times 10^{7}$ C.

$C = Q/V$

$Q = CV$

$= 25 \times 500$

12. A student connects an a.c. supply to an a.c. ammeter and a component **X**.

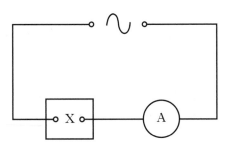

As the frequency of the a.c. supply is steadily increased, the ammeter reading also increases.

Component **X** is a

A   capacitor

B   diode

C   lamp

D   resistor

E   transistor.

13. An amplifier circuit is set up as shown.

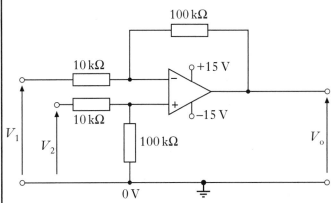

When $V_o = 0·60$ V and $V_1 = 2·70$ V, what is the value of V_2?

A   2·10 V

B   2·64 V

C   2·76 V

D   3·30 V

E   8·70 V

$V_2 = \dfrac{R_2}{R_1 + R_2} \times V_s$

[Turn over

$V_2 = \dfrac{100,000}{10,000 + 100,000} \times 15$

14. A prism is used to produce a spectrum from a source of white light as shown.

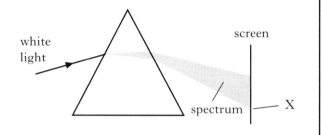

The colour observed at X is noted.

The prism is then replaced by a grating to produce spectra as shown.

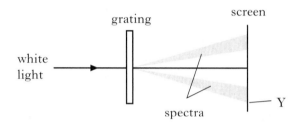

The colour observed at Y is noted.

Which row in the table gives the colour and wavelength of the light observed at X and the light observed at Y?

	Colour of light at X	Wavelength of light at X/nm	Colour of light at Y	Wavelength of light at Y/nm
A	Red	450	Red	450
B	Blue	450	Blue	450
C	Blue	650	Red	450
D	Blue	450	Red	650
E	Red	650	Blue	450

15. A ray of monochromatic light passes into a glass block as shown.

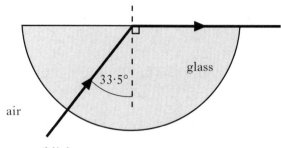

ray of light

The refractive index of the glass for this light is

A   0.03

B   0.55

C   0.87

D   1.20

E   1.81.

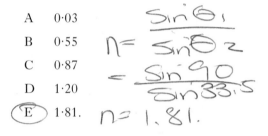

16. Which of the following statements about the characteristics of laser light is/are true?

I   It is monochromatic since all the photons have the same frequency.

II It is coherent because all the photons are in phase.

III Its irradiance is inversely proportional to the square of the distance from the source.

A   I only

B   I and II only

C   I and III only

D   II and III only

E   I, II and III

17. A student writes the following statements about p-type semiconductor material.

    I   Most charge carriers are positive.

    II The p-type material has a positive charge.

    III Impurity atoms in the material have 3 outer electrons.

    Which of these statements is/are true?

    A   I only

    B   II only

    C   I and II only

    D   I and III only

    E   I, II and III

18. A p-n junction diode is forward biased.

    Positive and negative charge carriers recombine in the junction region. This causes the emission of

    A   a hole

    B   an electron

    C   an electron-hole pair

    D   a proton

    E   a photon.

19. A sample of radioactive material has a mass of 20 g. There are 48 000 nuclear decays every minute in this sample.

    The activity of the sample is

    A   800 Bq

    B   2400 Bq

    C   48 000 Bq

    D   2 400 000 Bq

    E   2 880 000 Bq.

20. A sample of body tissue is irradiated by two different types of radiation, X and Y.

    The table gives the radiation weighting factor and absorbed dose for each radiation.

Type of radiation	Radiation weighting factor	Absorbed dose/μGy
X	10	5
Y	5	2

    The total equivalent dose received by the tissue is

    A $0 \cdot 9\,\mu$Sv

    B $4 \cdot 5\,\mu$Sv

    C $7 \cdot 0\,\mu$Sv

    D $40 \cdot 0\,\mu$Sv

    E $60 \cdot 0\,\mu$Sv.

    [Turn over

SECTION B

Write your answers to questions 21 to 30 in the answer book.

Marks

21. A basketball player throws a ball with an initial velocity of $6 \cdot 5 \, \text{m s}^{-1}$ at an angle of $50°$ to the horizontal. The ball is $2 \cdot 3 \, \text{m}$ above the ground when released.

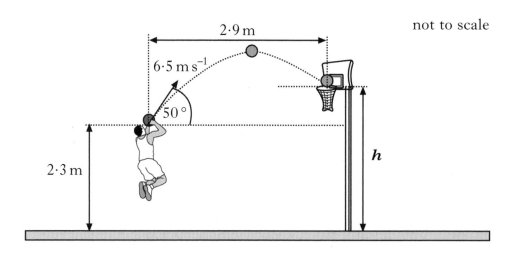

The ball travels a horizontal distance of $2 \cdot 9 \, \text{m}$ to reach the top of the basket. The effects of air resistance can be ignored.

(a) Calculate:

    (i)   the horizontal component of the initial velocity of the ball;   **1**

    (ii) the vertical component of the initial velocity of the ball.   **1**

(b) Show that the time taken for the ball to reach the basket is $0 \cdot 69 \, \text{s}$.   **1**

(c) Calculate the height h of the top of the basket.   **2**

(d) A student observing the player makes the following statement.

"The player should throw the ball with a higher speed at the same angle. The ball would then land in the basket as before but it would take a shorter time to travel the 2·9 metres."

Explain why the student's statement is incorrect.   **2**

    (7)

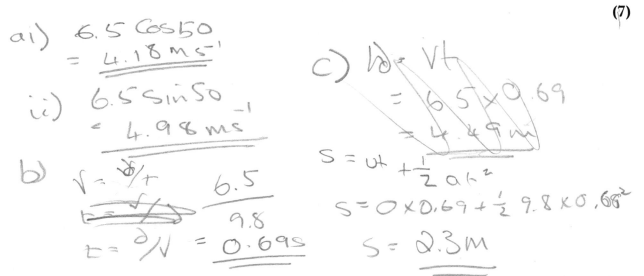

Marks

22. Golf clubs are tested to ensure they meet certain standards.

(a) In one test, a securely held clubhead is hit by a small steel pendulum. The time of contact between the clubhead and the pendulum is recorded.

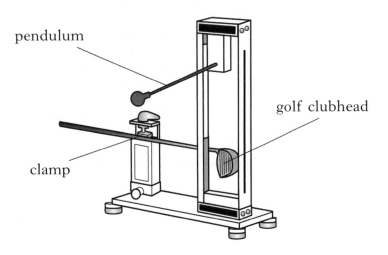

The experiment is repeated several times.

The results are shown.

248 μs   259 μs   251 μs   263 μs   254 μs

(i) Calculate:

    (A)   the mean contact time between the clubhead and the pendulum;   **1**

    (B)   the approximate absolute random uncertainty in this value.   **1**

(ii) In this test, the standard required is that the maximum value of the mean contact time must not be greater than 257 μs.

Does the club meet this standard?

You must justify your answer.   **1**

(b) In another test, a machine uses a club to hit a stationary golf ball.

The mass of the ball is $4 \cdot 5 \times 10^{-2}$ kg. The ball leaves the club with a speed of $50 \cdot 0$ m s^{-1}. The time of contact between the club and ball is 450 μs.

(i) Calculate the average force exerted on the ball by the club.   **2**

(ii) The test is repeated using a different club and an identical ball. The machine applies the same average force on the ball but with a longer contact time.

What effect, if any, does this have on the speed of the ball as it leaves the club?

Justify your answer.   **2**

    (7)

Marks

23. A student is training to become a diver.

(*a*) The student carries out an experiment to investigate the relationship between the pressure and volume of a fixed mass of gas using the apparatus shown.

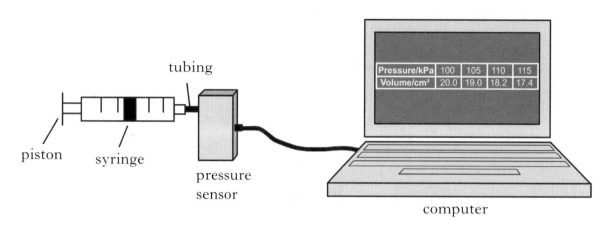

The pressure of the gas is recorded using a pressure sensor connected to a computer. The volume of the gas is also recorded. The student pushes the piston to alter the volume and a series of readings is taken.
The temperature of the gas is constant during the experiment.

The results are shown.

Pressure/kPa	100	105	110	115
Volume/cm³	20·0	19·0	18·2	17·4

    (i) Using **all** the data, establish the relationship between the pressure and volume of the gas. As $P\uparrow$ $V\downarrow$ $V\downarrow$ 2

    (ii) Use the kinetic model to explain the change in pressure as the volume of gas decreases.   2

(*b*) (i) The density of water in a loch is $1·02 \times 10^3\,\mathrm{kg\,m^{-3}}$. Atmospheric pressure is $1·01 \times 10^5\,\mathrm{Pa}$.

        Show that the **total** pressure at a depth of 12·0 m in this loch is $2·21 \times 10^5\,\mathrm{Pa}$.   2

    (ii) At the surface of the loch, the student breathes in a volume of $1·50 \times 10^{-3}\,\mathrm{m^3}$ of air.

        Calculate the volume this air would occupy at a depth of 12·0 m. The mass and temperature of the air are constant.   2

(*c*) At a depth of 12·0 m, the diver fills her lungs with air from her breathing apparatus. She then swims to the surface.

    Explain why it would be dangerous for her to hold her breath while doing this.   2

                                                                             (10)

Marks

24. A battery of e.m.f. 6·0 V and internal resistance, r, is connected to a variable resistor R as shown.

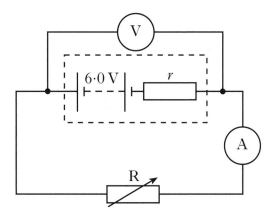

The graph shows how the current in the circuit changes as the resistance of R increases.

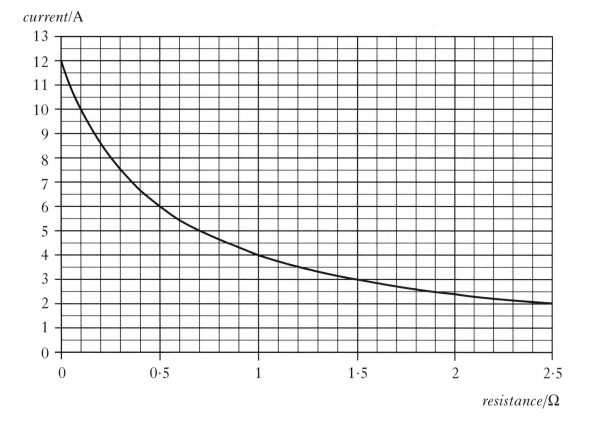

(a) Use information from the graph to calculate:

    (i)   the lost volts in the circuit when the resistance of R is 1·5 Ω;   **2**

    (ii)   the internal resistance, r, of the battery.   **2**

(b) The resistance of R is now increased.

    What effect, if any, does this have on the lost volts?

    You must justify your answer.   **2**

    (6)

Marks

25. (*a*) A microphone is connected to the input terminals of an oscilloscope.
A tuning fork is made to vibrate and held close to the microphone as shown.

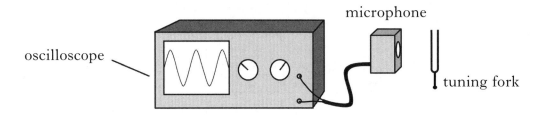

The following diagram shows the trace obtained and the settings on the oscilloscope.

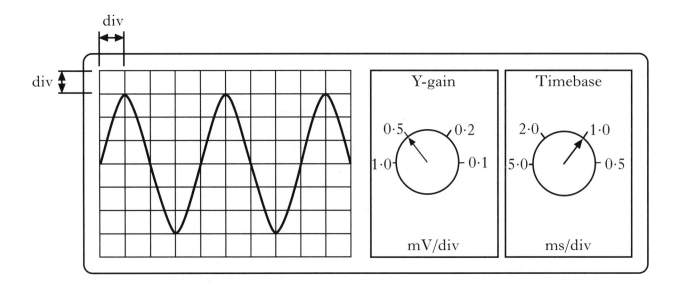

Calculate:

(i) the peak voltage of the signal; **1**

(ii) the frequency of the signal. **2**

Marks

25.   (continued)

   (*b*)   To amplify the signal from the microphone, it is connected to an op-amp circuit. The oscilloscope is now connected to the output of the amplifier as shown.

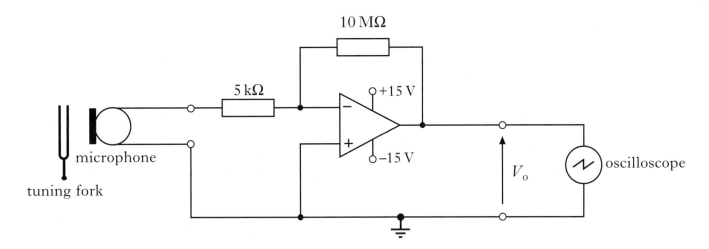

      The settings of the oscilloscope are adjusted to show a trace of the amplified signal.

     (i)   In which mode is this op-amp being used?   **1**

    (ii)   The peak voltage from the microphone is now 6·2 mV.

       Calculate the **r.m.s.** value of the output voltage, V_o, of the op-amp.   **3**

   (iii)   With the same input signal and settings on the oscilloscope, the supply voltage to the op-amp is now reduced from ± 15 V to ± 9 V.

       What effect does this change have on the trace on the oscilloscope?

       Justify your answer.   **2**

                                         (9)

[Turn over

Marks

26. A 12 volt battery of negligible internal resistance is connected in a circuit as shown.

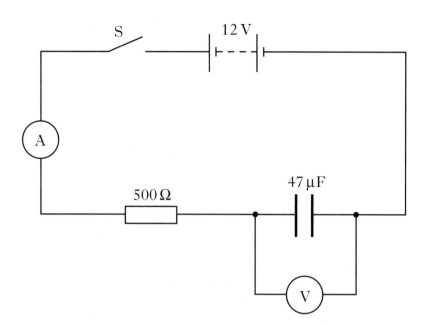

The capacitor is initially uncharged. Switch S is then closed and the capacitor starts to charge.

(*a*) Sketch a graph of the current against time from the instant switch S is closed. Numerical values are not required.   1

(*b*) At one instant during the charging of the capacitor the reading on the ammeter is 5·0 mA.

Calculate the reading on the voltmeter at this instant.   3

(*c*) Calculate the **maximum** energy stored in the capacitor in this circuit.   2

(*d*) The 500 Ω resistor is now replaced with a 2·0 kΩ resistor.

What effect, if any, does this have on the maximum energy stored in the capacitor?

Justify your answer.   2

(8)

Marks

27. A laser produces a narrow beam of monochromatic light.

(a) Red light from a laser passes through a grating as shown.

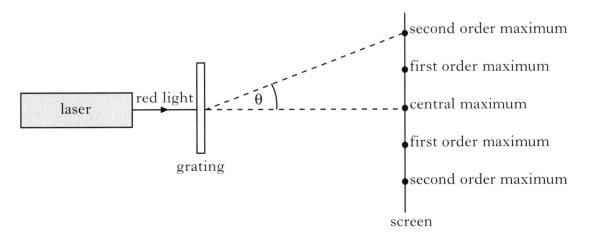

A series of maxima and minima is observed.

Explain in terms of waves how a **minimum** is produced. 1

(b) The laser is now replaced by a second laser, which emits blue light.

Explain why the observed maxima are now closer together. 1

(c) The wavelength of the blue light from the second laser is $4{\cdot}73 \times 10^{-7}\,\text{m}$. The spacing between the lines on the grating is $2{\cdot}00 \times 10^{-6}\,\text{m}$.

Calculate the angle between the central maximum and the second order maximum. 2

(4)

[Turn over

Marks

28. (a) Electrons which orbit the nucleus of an atom can be considered as occupying discrete energy levels.

The following diagram shows some of the energy levels for a particular atom.

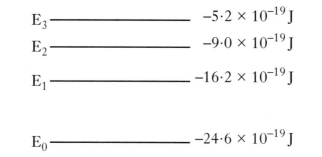

E_3 ——————————— $-5 \cdot 2 \times 10^{-19}$ J

E_2 ——————————— $-9 \cdot 0 \times 10^{-19}$ J

E_1 ——————————— $-16 \cdot 2 \times 10^{-19}$ J

E_0 ——————————— $-24 \cdot 6 \times 10^{-19}$ J

(i) Radiation is produced when electrons make transitions from a higher to a lower energy level.

Which transition, between these energy levels, produces radiation with the shortest wavelength?

Justify your answer. 2

(ii) An electron is excited from energy level E_2 to E_3 by absorbing light energy.

What frequency of light is used to excite this electron? 2

(b) Another source of light has a frequency of $4 \cdot 6 \times 10^{14}$ Hz in air.

A ray of this light is directed into a block of transparent material as shown.

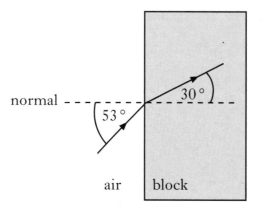

normal - - - - - - - - - - 30°
53°

air | block

Calculate the wavelength of the light in the block. 3

(7)

Marks

29. Ultraviolet radiation from a lamp is incident on the surface of a metal.

This causes the release of electrons from the surface of the metal.

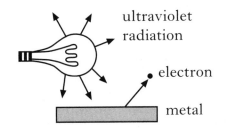

The energy of each photon of ultraviolet light is $5 \cdot 23 \times 10^{-19}$ J.

The work function of the metal is $2 \cdot 56 \times 10^{-19}$ J.

(a) Calculate:

   (i)   the maximum kinetic energy of an electron released from this metal by this radiation;   1

   (ii) the maximum speed of an emitted electron.   2

(b) The source of ultraviolet radiation is now moved further away from the surface of the metal.

   State the effect, if any, this has on the maximum speed of an emitted electron.

   Justify your answer.   2

   (5)

[Turn over

Marks

30. (*a*) Some power stations use nuclear fission reactions to provide energy for generating electricity. The following statement represents a fission reaction.

$$^{235}_{92}U \;+\; ^{1}_{0}n \;\rightarrow\; ^{139}_{57}La \;+\; ^{r}_{42}Mo \;+\; 2\,^{1}_{0}n \;+\; s\,^{0}_{-1}e$$

(i) Determine the numbers represented by the letters *r* and *s* in the above statement. **1**

(ii) Explain why a nuclear fission reaction releases energy. **1**

(iii) The masses of the particles involved in the reaction are shown in the table.

Particle	Mass/kg
$^{235}_{92}U$	$390 \cdot 173 \times 10^{-27}$
$^{139}_{57}La$	$230 \cdot 584 \times 10^{-27}$
$^{r}_{42}Mo$	$157 \cdot 544 \times 10^{-27}$
$^{1}_{0}n$	$1 \cdot 675 \times 10^{-27}$
$^{0}_{-1}e$	negligible

Calculate the energy released in this reaction. **3**

Marks

30. **(continued)**

(*b*) One method of reducing the radiation received by a person is by using lead shielding.

In an investigation of the absorption of gamma radiation by lead, the following graph of corrected count rate against thickness of lead is obtained.

corrected count rate/counts per minute

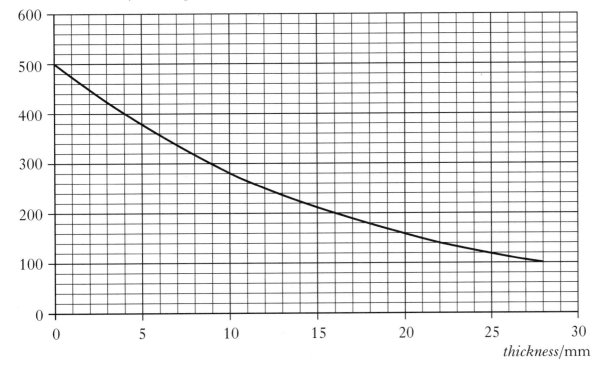

(i) Determine the half-value thickness of lead for this radiation.   **1**

(ii) With no shielding, the equivalent dose rate a short distance from this source is $200\,\mu\mathrm{Sv}\,\mathrm{h}^{-1}$.

When the source is stored in a lead container, the equivalent dose rate at the same distance falls to $50\,\mu\mathrm{Sv}\,\mathrm{h}^{-1}$.

Calculate the thickness of the lead container.   **1**

(7)

[END OF QUESTION PAPER]

[BLANK PAGE]

HIGHER

2010

[BLANK PAGE]

X069/301

NATIONAL QUALIFICATIONS 2010	FRIDAY, 28 MAY 1.00 PM – 3.30 PM	PHYSICS HIGHER

Read Carefully

Reference may be made to the Physics Data Booklet.

1 All questions should be attempted.

Section A (questions 1 to 20)

2 Check that the answer sheet is for Physics Higher (Section A).

3 For this section of the examination you must use an **HB pencil** and, where necessary, an eraser.

4 Check that the answer sheet you have been given has **your name**, **date of birth**, **SCN** (Scottish Candidate Number) and **Centre Name** printed on it.

  Do not change any of these details.

5 If any of this information is wrong, tell the Invigilator immediately.

6 If this information is correct, **print** your name and seat number in the boxes provided.

7 There is **only one correct** answer to each question.

8 Any rough working should be done on the question paper or the rough working sheet, **not** on your answer sheet.

9 At the end of the exam, put the **answer sheet for Section A inside the front cover of your answer book**.

10 Instructions as to how to record your answers to questions 1–20 are given on page three.

Section B (questions 21 to 30)

11 Answer the questions numbered 21 to 30 in the answer book provided.

12 **All answers must be written clearly and legibly in ink**.

13 Fill in the details on the front of the answer book.

14 Enter the question number clearly in the margin of the answer book beside each of your answers to questions 21 to 30.

15 Care should be taken to give an appropriate number of significant figures in the final answers to calculations.

16 Where additional paper, eg square ruled paper, is used, write your name and SCN (Scottish Candidate Number) on it and place it inside the front cover of your answer booklet.

DATA SHEET
COMMON PHYSICAL QUANTITIES

Quantity	Symbol	Value	Quantity	Symbol	Value
Speed of light in vacuum	c	$3\!\cdot\!00 \times 10^{8}$ m s^{-1}	Mass of electron	m_e	$9\!\cdot\!11 \times 10^{-31}$ kg
Magnitude of the charge on an electron	e	$1\!\cdot\!60 \times 10^{-19}$ C	Mass of neutron	m_n	$1\!\cdot\!675 \times 10^{-27}$ kg
Gravitational acceleration on Earth	g	$9\!\cdot\!8$ m s^{-2}	Mass of proton	m_p	$1\!\cdot\!673 \times 10^{-27}$ kg
Planck's constant	h	$6\!\cdot\!63 \times 10^{-34}$ J s			

REFRACTIVE INDICES
The refractive indices refer to sodium light of wavelength 589 nm and to substances at a temperature of 273 K.

Substance	Refractive index	Substance	Refractive index
Diamond	2·42	Water	1·33
Crown glass	1·50	Air	1·00

SPECTRAL LINES

Element	Wavelength/nm	Colour	Element	Wavelength/nm	Colour
Hydrogen	656	Red	Cadmium	644	Red
	486	Blue-green		509	Green
	434	Blue-violet		480	Blue
	410	Violet			
	397	Ultraviolet			
	389	Ultraviolet			
Sodium	589	Yellow			

Lasers

Element	Wavelength/nm	Colour
Carbon dioxide	9550 10590	Infrared
Helium-neon	633	Red

PROPERTIES OF SELECTED MATERIALS

Substance	Density/ kg m^{-3}	Melting Point/ K	Boiling Point/ K
Aluminium	$2\!\cdot\!70 \times 10^{3}$	933	2623
Copper	$8\!\cdot\!96 \times 10^{3}$	1357	2853
Ice	$9\!\cdot\!20 \times 10^{2}$	273	. . . .
Sea Water	$1\!\cdot\!02 \times 10^{3}$	264	377
Water	$1\!\cdot\!00 \times 10^{3}$	273	373
Air	$1\!\cdot\!29$	. . . .	. . . .
Hydrogen	$9\!\cdot\!0 \times 10^{-2}$	14	20

The gas densities refer to a temperature of 273 K and a pressure of $1\!\cdot\!01 \times 10^{5}$ Pa.

SECTION A

For questions 1 to 20 in this section of the paper the answer to each question is either A, B, C, D or E. Decide what your answer is, then, using your pencil, put a horizontal line in the space provided—see the example below.

EXAMPLE

The energy unit measured by the electricity meter in your home is the

    A kilowatt-hour

    B ampere

    C watt

    D coulomb

    E volt.

The correct answer is **A**—kilowatt-hour. The answer **A** has been clearly marked in **pencil** with a horizontal line (see below).

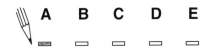

Changing an answer

If you decide to change your answer, carefully erase your first answer and, using your pencil, fill in the answer you want. The answer below has been changed to **E**.

[Turn over

SECTION A

Answer questions 1–20 on the answer sheet.

1. Acceleration is the change in

   A   distance per unit time

   B   displacement per unit time

   C   velocity per unit distance

   D   speed per unit time

   E   velocity per unit time.

Acc

2. The graph shows how the acceleration, a, of an object varies with time, t.

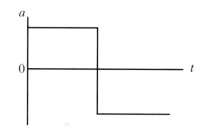

Which graph shows how the velocity, v, of the object varies with time, t?

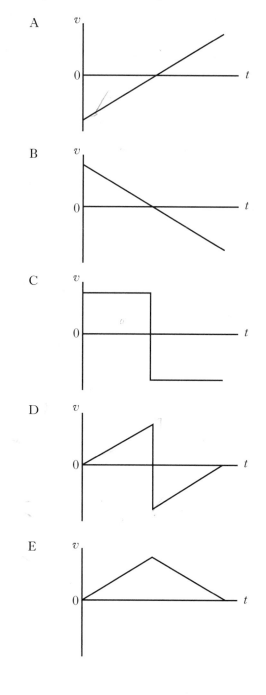

3. A car of mass 1000 kg is travelling at a speed of 40 m s^{-1} along a race track. The brakes are applied and the speed of the car decreases to 10 m s^{-1}.

How much kinetic energy is lost by the car?

A   15 kJ

B   50 kJ

C   450 kJ

D   750 kJ

E   800 kJ

4. A substance can exist as a solid, a liquid or a gas.

Which row in the table shows the approximate relative magnitudes of the densities of the substance in these states?

	Density of solid	Density of liquid	Density of gas
A	1000	1000	1
B	10	10	1000
C	1	1	1000
D	1000	10	1
E	1	1	10

5. A fish is swimming at a depth of 10·4 m.

The density of the water is $1·03 \times 10^3$ kg m^{-3}.

The pressure at this depth caused by the water is

A $0·99 \times 10^2$ Pa

B $1·04 \times 10^4$ Pa

C $1·07 \times 10^4$ Pa

D $1·05 \times 10^5$ Pa

E $1·07 \times 10^5$ Pa.

6. Ice at a temperature of −10 °C is heated until it becomes water at 80 °C.

The temperature change in kelvin is

A   70 K

B   90 K

C   343 K

D   363 K

E   636 K.

7. The potential difference between two points is

A   the work done in moving one electron between the two points

B   the voltage between the two points when there is a current of one ampere

C   the work done in moving one coulomb of charge between the two points

D   the kinetic energy gained by an electron as it moves between the two points

E   the work done in moving any charge between the two points.

8. The product, X, of a nuclear reaction passes through an electric field as shown.

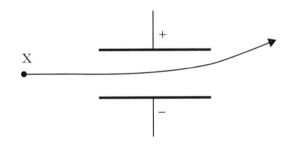

Product X is

A   an alpha particle

B   a beta particle

C   gamma radiation

D   a fast neutron

E   a slow neutron.

[Turn over

9. Which of the following combinations of resistors has the greatest resistance between X and Y?

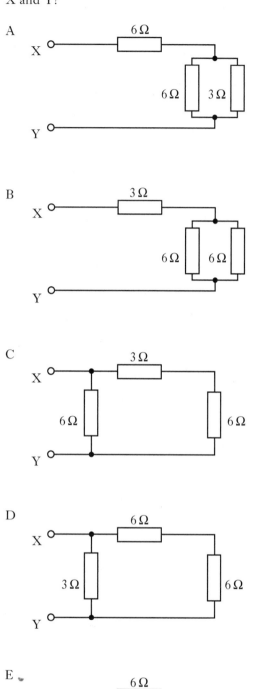

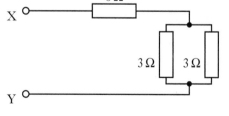

10. In the following Wheatstone bridge circuit, the reading on the voltmeter is zero when the resistance of R is set at $1\,k\Omega$.

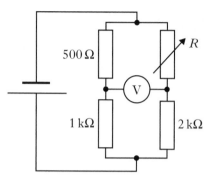

Which of the following is the graph of the voltmeter reading V against the resistance R?

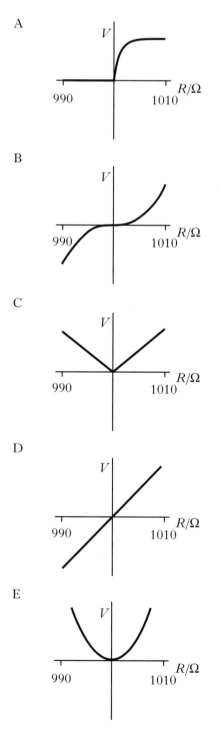

11. A student makes the following statements about capacitors.

    I   Capacitors block a.c. signals.

    II   Capacitors store energy.

    III   Capacitors store charge.

Which of these statements is/are true?

A   I only

B   I and II only

C   I and III only

D   II and III only

E   I, II and III

12. A circuit is set up as shown.

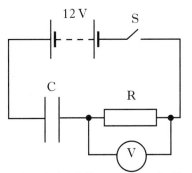

The capacitor is initially uncharged. Switch S is now closed. Which graph shows how the potential difference, V, across R, varies with time, t?

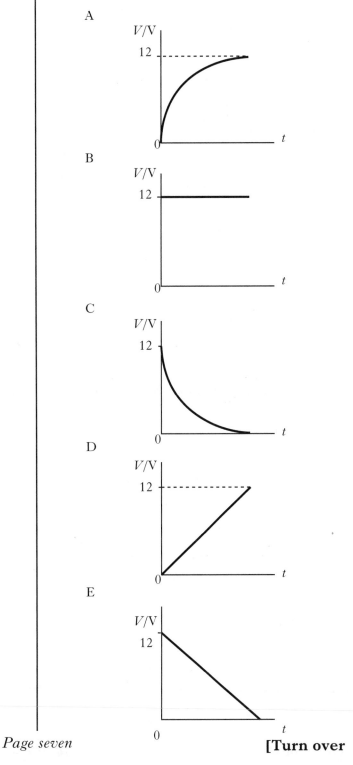

13. An op-amp is connected in a circuit as shown.

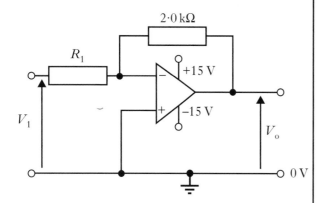

The input voltage V_1 is 0.50 V.

Which row in the table shows possible values for R_1 and V_o?

	R_1/kΩ	V_o/V
A	1.0	1.0
B	4.0	1.0
C	1.0	-0.25
D	4.0	-1.0
E	1.0	-1.0

14. Photons of energy 7.0×10^{-19} J are incident on a clean metal surface. The work function of the metal is 9.0×10^{-19} J.

Which of the following is correct?

A No electrons are emitted from the metal.

B Electrons with a maximum kinetic energy of 2.0×10^{-19} J are emitted from the metal.

C Electrons with a maximum kinetic energy of 7.0×10^{-19} J are emitted from the metal.

D Electrons with a maximum kinetic energy of 9.0×10^{-19} J are emitted from the metal.

E Electrons with a maximum kinetic energy of 16×10^{-19} J are emitted from the metal.

15. The diagram represents some of the energy levels for an atom of a gas.

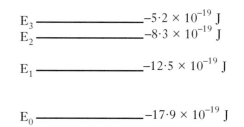

E_3	-5.2×10^{-19} J
E_2	-8.3×10^{-19} J
E_1	-12.5×10^{-19} J
E_0	-17.9×10^{-19} J

White light passes through the gas and absorption lines are observed in the spectrum.

Which electron transition produces the absorption line corresponding to the lowest frequency?

A E_3 to E_2

B E_2 to E_3

C E_1 to E_0

D E_0 to E_1

E E_0 to E_3

16. An LED is connected as shown.

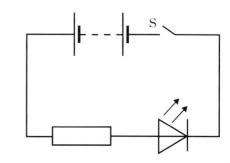

When switch S is closed

A the p-n junction is reverse biased and free charge carriers are produced which may recombine to give quanta of radiation

B the p-n junction is forward biased and positive and negative charge carriers are produced by the action of light

C the p-n junction is reverse biased and positive and negative charge carriers are produced by the action of light

D the p-n junction is forward biased and positive and negative charge carriers may recombine to give quanta of radiation

E the p-n junction is reverse biased and positive and negative charge carriers may recombine to give quanta of radiation.

17. The diagram represents the structure of an n-channel enhancement MOSFET.

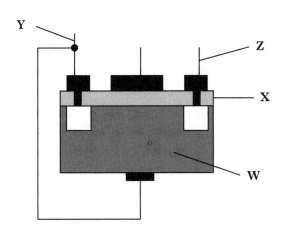

Which row in the table gives the names for the parts labelled **W**, **X**, **Y** and **Z**?

	W	X	Y	Z
A	substrate	implant	source	drain
B	implant	substrate	source	drain
C	substrate	oxide layer	drain	source
D	implant	substrate	gate	source
E	substrate	oxide layer	source	drain

18. The following statement describes a fusion reaction.

$$^2_1H + {}^2_1H \longrightarrow {}^3_2He + {}^1_0n + energy$$

The total mass of the particles before the reaction is $6\cdot684 \times 10^{-27}$ kg.

The total mass of the particles after the reaction is $6\cdot680 \times 10^{-27}$ kg.

The energy released in this reaction is

A $6\cdot012 \times 10^{-10}$ J

B $6\cdot016 \times 10^{-10}$ J

C $1\cdot800 \times 10^{-13}$ J

D $3\cdot600 \times 10^{-13}$ J

E $1\cdot200 \times 10^{-21}$ J.

19. A sample of tissue receives an equivalent dose of 40 mSv from a beam of neutrons.

The neutrons have a radiation weighting factor of 10.

The energy absorbed by the tissue is 100 μJ.

The mass of the tissue is

A $2\cdot5 \times 10^{-4}$ kg

B $2\cdot5 \times 10^{-2}$ kg

C $4\cdot0$ kg

D 40 kg

E $4\cdot0 \times 10^{3}$ kg.

20. A sample of tissue is placed near a source of gamma radiation. The equivalent dose rate for the tissue is 80 μSv h^{-1}.

The equivalent dose rate is now reduced to 10 μSv h^{-1} by placing lead shielding between the source and the tissue.

The half value thickness of lead is 8·0 mm for this source.

The thickness of the lead shielding is

A   1·0 mm

B   8·0 mm

C   24 mm

D   64 mm

E   80 mm.

[Turn over

Mark:

SECTION B

Write your answers to questions 21 to 30 in the answer book.

21. A helicopter is flying at a constant height above the ground. The helicopter is carrying a crate suspended from a cable as shown.

(a) The helicopter flies 20 km on a bearing of 180 (due South). It then turns on to a bearing of 140 (50° South of East) and travels a further 30 km.

The helicopter takes 15 minutes to travel the 50 km.

  (i) By scale drawing (or otherwise) find the resultant displacement of the helicopter. **2**

  (ii) Calculate the average velocity of the helicopter during the 15 minutes. **2**

(b) The helicopter reaches its destination and hovers above a drop zone.

  (i) The total mass of the helicopter and crate is $1 \cdot 21 \times 10^4$ kg.

  Show that the helicopter produces a lift force of 119 kN. **1**

  (ii) The helicopter now drops the crate which has a mass of $2 \cdot 30 \times 10^3$ kg. The lift force remains constant.

  Describe the vertical motion of the helicopter immediately after the crate is dropped.

  Justify your answer in terms of the forces acting on the helicopter. **2**

  (7)

Marks

22. The apparatus shown is set up to investigate collisions between two vehicles on a track.

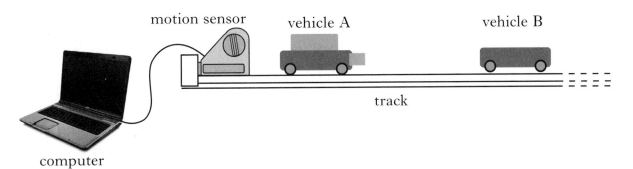

The mass of vehicle A is 0·22 kg and the mass of vehicle B is 0·16 kg.

The effects of friction are negligible.

(a) During one experiment the vehicles collide and stick together. The computer connected to the motion sensor displays the velocity-time graph for vehicle A.

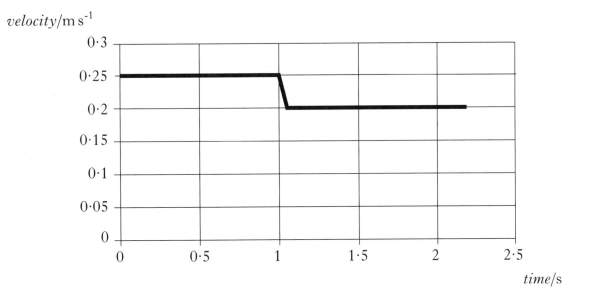

(i) State the law of conservation of momentum.   1

(ii) Calculate the velocity of vehicle B before the collision.   2

(b) The same apparatus is used to carry out a second experiment.

In this experiment, vehicle B is stationary before the collision.

Vehicle A has the same velocity before the collision as in the first experiment.

After the collision, the two vehicles stick together.

Is their combined velocity less than, equal to, or greater than that in the first collision?

Justify your answer.   2

(5)

Mark

23. (*a*) A gymnast of mass 40 kg is practising on a trampoline.

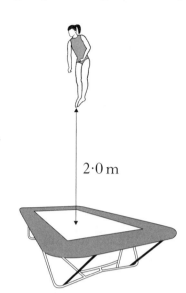

2·0 m

(i) At maximum height the gymnast's feet are 2·0 m above the trampoline. Show that the speed of the gymnast, as she lands on the trampoline, is 6·3 m s^{-1}.

1

(ii) The gymnast rebounds with a speed of 5·7 m s^{-1}. Calculate the change in momentum of the gymnast.

2

(iii) The gymnast was in contact with the trampoline for 0·50 s. Calculate the average force exerted by the trampoline on the gymnast.

2

Marks

23. (continued)

(b) Another gymnast is practising on a piece of equipment called the rings. The gymnast grips two wooden rings suspended above the gym floor by strong, vertical ropes as shown in Figure 1.

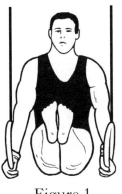

Figure 1

He now stretches out his arms until each rope makes an angle of 10° with the vertical as shown in Figure 2.

Figure 2

Explain why the tension in each rope increases as the gymnast stretches out his arms.

2

(7)

[Turn over

Mark

24. An experiment is carried out to measure the time taken for a steel ball to fall vertically through a fixed distance using an electronic timer.

(*a*) The experiment is repeated and the following values for time recorded.

0·49 s,   0·53 s,   0·50 s,   0·50 s,   0·55 s,   0·51 s.

Calculate:

(i) the mean value of the time;   **1**

(ii) the approximate random uncertainty in the mean value of the time.   **1**

(*b*) Part of the circuit in the electronic timer consists of a 1·6 mF capacitor and an 18 kΩ resistor connected to a switch and a 4·5 V supply.

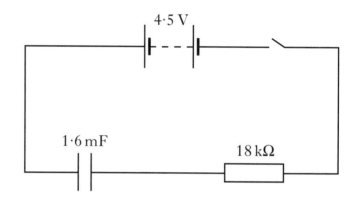

(i) Calculate the charge on the capacitor when it is fully charged.   **2**

(ii) Sketch the graph of the current in the resistor against time as the capacitor charges.

Numerical values are required on the current axis.   **2**

(6)

Marks

25. The headlights on a truck are switched on automatically when a light sensor detects the light level falling below a certain value.

The light sensor consists of an LDR connected in a Wheatstone bridge as shown.

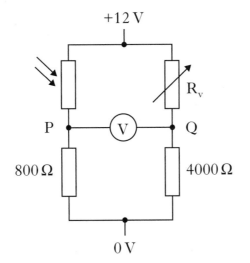

   (a) The variable resistor, R_v, is set at $6000\,\Omega$.

      (i) Calculate the resistance of the LDR when the bridge is balanced.   **2**

      (ii) As the light level decreases, the resistance of the LDR increases. Calculate the reading on the voltmeter when the resistance of the LDR is $1600\,\Omega$.   **2**

   (b) The Wheatstone bridge is connected to an op-amp as shown. The output of the op-amp controls the headlights circuit.

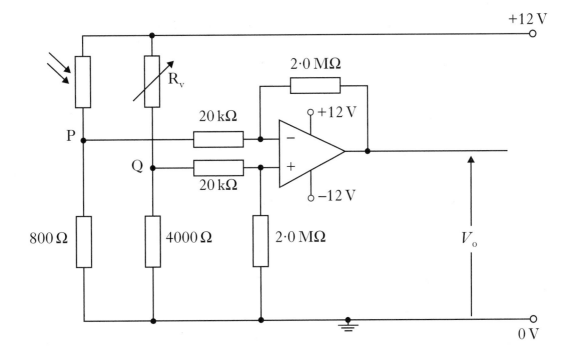

The resistance of R_v is adjusted so that the potential at Q is $3\cdot2\,V$. At a particular light level, the potential at P is $3\cdot0\,V$. Determine the output voltage, V_o, of the op-amp.   **3**

                                                                     (7)

Mark

26. A signal generator is connected to a lamp, a resistor and an ammeter in series. An oscilloscope is connected across the output terminals of the signal generator.

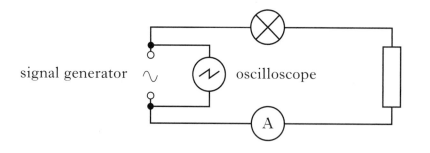

The oscilloscope control settings and the trace displayed on its screen are shown.

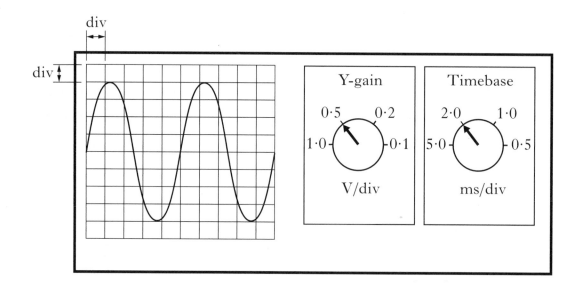

(a) For this signal calculate:

(i) the peak voltage; **1**

(ii) the frequency. **2**

(b) The frequency is now doubled. The peak voltage of the signal is kept constant.

State what happens to the reading on the ammeter. **1**

(c) The resistor is now replaced by a capacitor.

The procedure in part (b) is repeated.

State what happens to the reading on the ammeter as the frequency is doubled. **1**

(d) The capacitor will be damaged if the potential difference across it exceeds 16 V.

The capacitor is now removed from this circuit and connected to a different a.c. supply of output 15 V$_{r.m.s.}$.

Explain whether or not the capacitor is damaged. **2**

(7)

Marks

27. A student is carrying out an experiment to investigate the interference of sound waves. She sets up the following apparatus.

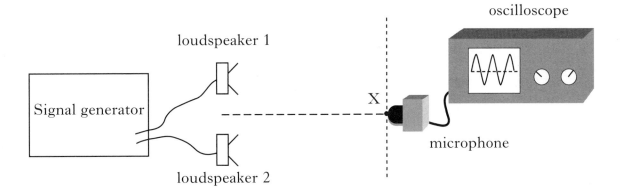

The microphone is initially placed at point X which is the same distance from each loudspeaker. A maximum is detected at X.

(*a*) The microphone is now moved to the first minimum at Y as shown.

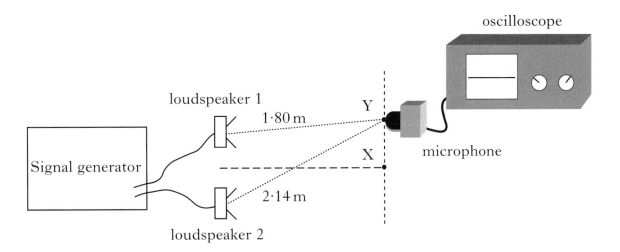

Calculate the wavelength of the sound waves.   2

(*b*) Loudspeaker 1 is now disconnected.

What happens to the amplitude of the sound detected by the microphone at Y?

Explain your answer.   2

                                                              (4)

[Turn over

Mark

28. A garden spray consists of a tank, a pump and a spray nozzle.

spray nozzle

pump

tank

The tank is partially filled with water.

The pump is then used to increase the pressure of the air above the water.

(a) The volume of the compressed air in the tank is $1 \cdot 60 \times 10^{-3} \, m^3$.

The surface area of the water is $3 \cdot 00 \times 10^{-2} \, m^2$.

The pressure of the air in the tank is $4 \cdot 60 \times 10^5 \, Pa$.

   (i) Calculate the force on the surface of the water.   **2**

  (ii) The spray nozzle is operated and water is pushed out until the pressure of the air in the tank is $1 \cdot 00 \times 10^5 \, Pa$.

      Calculate the volume of water expelled.   **3**

(b) The gardener observes a spectrum when sunlight illuminates the drops of water in the spray. This is because each drop of water is acting as a prism.

The diagram shows the path taken by light of wavelength 650 nm through a drop of water.

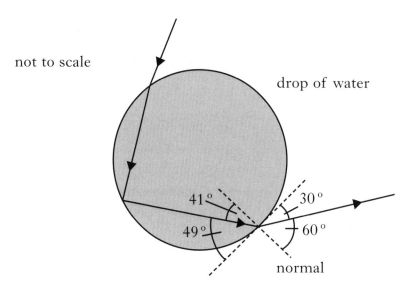

not to scale

drop of water

41°

49°

30°

60°

normal

   (i) What happens to the frequency of this light when it enters the drop of water?   **1**

Marks

28. (*b*) **(continued)**

    (ii) Using information from the diagram, calculate the refractive index of the water for this wavelength of light.   **2**

    (iii) Calculate the critical angle for this wavelength of light in the water.   **2**

    (iv) Light of shorter wavelength also passes through the drop of water.

        Will the critical angle for this light be less than, equal to, or greater than that for light of wavelength 650 nm?

        Justify your answer.   **2**

                                                                 (12)

[Turn over

Mark

29. A laser produces a beam of light with a frequency of $4{\cdot}74 \times 10^{14}\,\text{Hz}$.

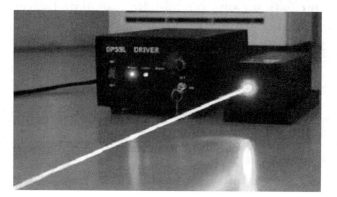

(a) The laser has a power of $0{\cdot}10\,\text{mW}$. Explain why light from this laser can cause eye damage.   **1**

(b) Calculate the energy of each photon in the laser beam.   **2**

(c) Inside the laser, photons stimulate the emission of more photons.

State **two** ways in which the stimulated photons are identical to the photons producing them.   **1**

(d) This laser beam is now incident on a grating as shown below.

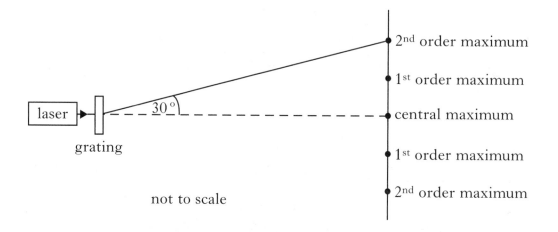

The second order maximum is detected at an angle of $30\,^\circ$ from the central maximum.

Calculate the separation of the slits on the grating.   **3**

(7)

Marks

30. A smoke alarm contains a very small sample of the radioactive isotope Americium-241, represented by the symbol

$$^{241}_{95}\text{Am}$$

(a) How many neutrons are there in a nucleus of this isotope?   1

(b) This isotope decays by emitting alpha particles as shown in the following statement.

$$^{241}_{95}\text{Am} \longrightarrow {}^{s}_{r}T + \alpha$$

   (i) Determine the numbers represented by the letters *r* and *s*.   1

   (ii) Use the data booklet to identify the element *T*.   1

(c) The activity of the radioactive sample is 30 kBq. How many decays take place in one minute?   2

(d) The alarm circuit in the smoke detector contains a battery of e.m.f. 9·0 V and internal resistance 2·0 Ω.

This circuit is shown.

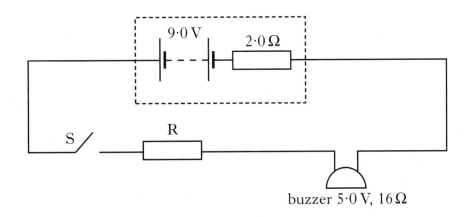

When smoke is detected, switch S closes and the buzzer operates. The buzzer has a resistance of 16 Ω and an operating voltage of 5·0 V.

Calculate the value pof resistor R required in this circuit.   3

(8)

[END OF QUESTION PAPER]

[BLANK PAGE]

HIGHER

2011

[BLANK PAGE]

X069/301

NATIONAL QUALIFICATIONS 2011	MONDAY, 23 MAY 1.00 PM – 3.30 PM	PHYSICS HIGHER

Read Carefully

Reference may be made to the Physics Data Booklet.

1 All questions should be attempted.

Section A (questions 1 to 20)

2 Check that the answer sheet is for Physics Higher (Section A).

3 For this section of the examination you must use an **HB pencil** and, where necessary, an eraser.

4 Check that the answer sheet you have been given has **your name**, **date of birth**, **SCN** (Scottish Candidate Number) and **Centre Name** printed on it.

Do not change any of these details.

5 If any of this information is wrong, tell the Invigilator immediately.

6 If this information is correct, **print** your name and seat number in the boxes provided.

7 There is **only one correct** answer to each question.

8 Any rough working should be done on the question paper or the rough working sheet, **not** on your answer sheet.

9 At the end of the exam, put the **answer sheet for Section A inside the front cover of your answer book**.

10 Instructions as to how to record your answers to questions 1–20 are given on page three.

Section B (questions 21 to 30)

11 Answer the questions numbered 21 to 30 in the answer book provided.

12 **All answers must be written clearly and legibly in ink**.

13 Fill in the details on the front of the answer book.

14 Enter the question number clearly in the margin of the answer book beside each of your answers to questions 21 to 30.

15 Care should be taken to give an appropriate number of significant figures in the final answers to calculations.

16 Where additional paper, eg square ruled paper, is used, write your name and SCN (Scottish Candidate Number) on it and place it inside the front cover of your answer booklet.

DATA SHEET
COMMON PHYSICAL QUANTITIES

Quantity	Symbol	Value	Quantity	Symbol	Value
Speed of light in vacuum	c	3.00×10^8 m s^{-1}	Mass of electron	m_e	9.11×10^{-31} kg
Magnitude of the charge on an electron	e	1.60×10^{-19} C	Mass of neutron	m_n	1.675×10^{-27} kg
Gravitational acceleration on Earth	g	9.8 m s^{-2}	Mass of proton	m_p	1.673×10^{-27} kg
Planck's constant	h	6.63×10^{-34} J s			

REFRACTIVE INDICES

The refractive indices refer to sodium light of wavelength 589 nm and to substances at a temperature of 273 K.

Substance	Refractive index	Substance	Refractive index
Diamond	2·42	Water	1·33
Crown glass	1·50	Air	1·00

SPECTRAL LINES

Element	Wavelength/nm	Colour	Element	Wavelength/nm	Colour
Hydrogen	656	Red	Cadmium	644	Red
	486	Blue-green		509	Green
	434	Blue-violet		480	Blue
	410	Violet			
	397	Ultraviolet			
	389	Ultraviolet			
Sodium	589	Yellow			

Lasers

Element	Wavelength/nm	Colour
Carbon dioxide	9550 } 10590 }	Infrared
Helium-neon	633	Red

PROPERTIES OF SELECTED MATERIALS

Substance	Density/kg m^{-3}	Melting Point/K	Boiling Point/K
Aluminium	2.70×10^3	933	2623
Copper	8.96×10^3	1357	2853
Ice	9.20×10^2	273	....
Sea Water	1.02×10^3	264	377
Water	1.00×10^3	273	373
Air	1·29	....	....
Hydrogen	9.0×10^{-2}	14	20

The gas densities refer to a temperature of 273 K and a pressure of 1.01×10^5 Pa.

SECTION A

For questions 1 to 20 in this section of the paper the answer to each question is either A, B, C, D or E. Decide what your answer is, then, using your pencil, put a horizontal line in the space provided—see the example below.

EXAMPLE

The energy unit measured by the electricity meter in your home is the

    A kilowatt-hour

    B ampere

    C watt

    D coulomb

    E volt.

The correct answer is **A**—kilowatt-hour. The answer **A** has been clearly marked in **pencil** with a horizontal line (see below).

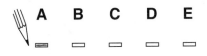

Changing an answer

If you decide to change your answer, carefully erase your first answer and, using your pencil, fill in the answer you want. The answer below has been changed to **E**.

[Turn over

SECTION A

Answer questions 1–20 on the answer sheet.

1. Which of the following is a scalar quantity?

   A   velocity

   B   acceleration

   (C) mass

   D   force

   E   momentum

2. A vehicle is travelling in a straight line. Graphs of velocity and acceleration against time are shown.

   Which pair of graphs could represent the motion of the vehicle?

   A   *velocity*   *acceleration*

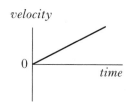

   B   *velocity*   *acceleration*

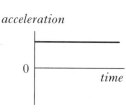

   C   *velocity*   *acceleration*

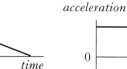

   D   *velocity*   *acceleration*

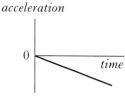

   (E)   *velocity*   *acceleration*

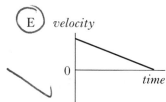

3. A car of mass 1200 kg pulls a horsebox of mass 700 kg along a straight, horizontal road.

   They have an acceleration of $2 \cdot 0 \, \mathrm{m\,s^{-2}}$.

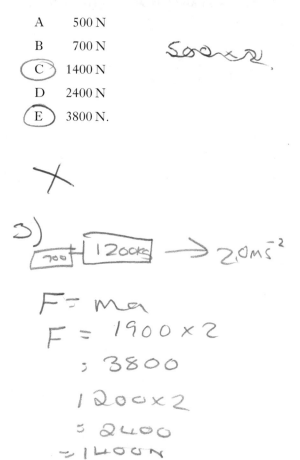

   Assuming that the frictional forces are negligible, the tension in the coupling between the car and the horsebox is

   A   500 N

   B   700 N

   (C) 1400 N

   D   2400 N

   (E)   3800 N.

4. Two trolleys travel towards each other in a straight line along a frictionless surface.

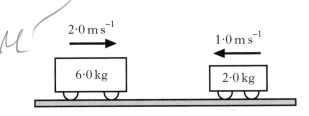

The trolleys collide. After the collision the trolleys move as shown below.

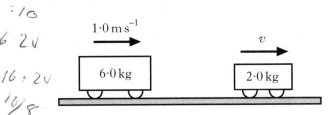

Which row in the table gives the total momentum and the total kinetic energy **after** the collision?

Total momentum/ kg m s^{-1}	Total kinetic energy/ J
A	10	7·0
B	10	13
C	10	20
D	14	13
E	14	7·0

(handwritten:) 12 + 2 = 16 ; 6 2v ; 16 = 2v ; 16/8 ; +2 t = 10

5. An aircraft cruises at an altitude at which the external air pressure is 0.40×10^5 Pa. The air pressure inside the aircraft cabin is maintained at 1.0×10^5 Pa. The area of an external cabin door is $2.0 \,\text{m}^2$.

What is the outward force on the door due to the pressure difference?

A 0.30×10^5 N
B 0.70×10^5 N
C 1.2×10^5 N
D 2.0×10^5 N
E 2.8×10^5 N

(handwritten:) $P = \frac{F}{a}$; $F = Pa$; $0.6 \times 10^5 \times 2 = 1 \times 10^5$; 40,000

6. A cylinder of height 1·0 m is held stationary in a swimming pool. The top of the cylinder is at a depth of 1·5 m below the surface of the water.

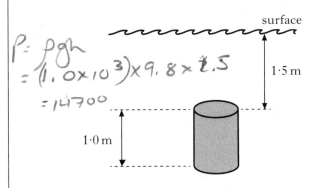

The density of the water is $1.0 \times 10^3 \,\text{kg m}^{-3}$.

The pressure due to the water exerted on the top surface of the cylinder is

A 1.5×10^3 N m^{-2}
B 4.9×10^3 N m^{-2}
C 9.8×10^3 N m^{-2}
D 14.7×10^3 N m^{-2}
E 24.5×10^3 N m^{-2}.

(handwritten:) $P = \rho g h = (1.0 \times 10^3) \times 9.8 \times 1.5 = 14700$; $\rho = m/V$; $= 2.5 m$; $1.0 \times 10^3 \times 2.5 \times 9.8$

7. A fixed mass of gas is heated inside a rigid container. As its temperature changes from T_1 to T_2 the pressure increases from 1.0×10^5 Pa to 2.0×10^5 Pa.

Which row in the table shows possible values for T_1 and T_2?

	T_1	T_2
A	27 °C	327 °C
B	30 °C	60 °C
C	80 °C	40 °C
D	303 K	333 K
E	600 K	300 K

(handwritten:) $\frac{P_1}{T_1} = \frac{P_2}{T_2}$; $\frac{1 \times 10^5}{T_1} = \frac{2 \times 10^5}{T_2}$; $\frac{P_1}{T_1} = \frac{P_2}{T_2}$; $\frac{1 \times 10^5}{T_1} = \frac{2 \times 10^5}{T_2}$

[Turn over

8. One volt is equivalent to one

   A   farad per coulomb

   B   ampere per ohm

   C   joule per ampere

   D   joule per ohm

   E   joule per coulomb.

9. A Wheatstone bridge circuit is set up as shown.

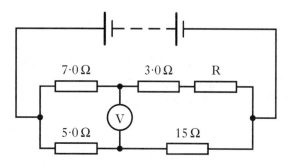

The reading on the voltmeter is zero.

The value of resistor R is

   A $3 \cdot 0\,\Omega$

   B $4 \cdot 0\,\Omega$

   C $18\,\Omega$

   D $21\,\Omega$

   E $24\,\Omega$.

10. A Wheatstone bridge circuit is set up as shown.

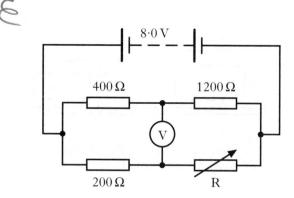

When the variable resistor R is set at $600\,\Omega$ the bridge is balanced. When R is set at $601\,\Omega$ the reading on the voltmeter is $+2 \cdot 5\,mV$.

R is now set at $598\,\Omega$.

The reading on the voltmeter is

   A $-7 \cdot 5\,mV$

   B $-5 \cdot 0\,mV$

   C $-2 \cdot 5\,mV$

   D $+5 \cdot 0\,mV$

   E $+7 \cdot 5\,mV$.

11. The output of a 50 Hz a.c. supply is connected to the input of an oscilloscope. The trace produced on the screen of the oscilloscope is shown.

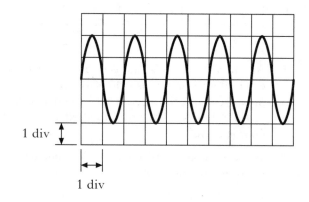

The time-base control of the oscilloscope is set at

   A   1 ms/div

   B   10 ms/div

   C   20 ms/div

   D   100 ms/div

   E   200 ms/div.

12. An a.c. supply with an output voltage of $6·0$ V r.m.s. is connected to a $3·0\,\Omega$ resistor.

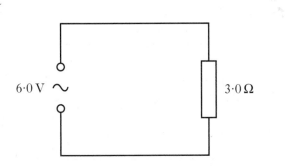

Which row in the table shows the peak voltage across the resistor and the peak current in the circuit?

	Peak voltage/V	Peak current/A
A	$6\sqrt{2}$	$2\sqrt{2}$
B	$6\sqrt{2}$	2
C	6	2
D	$\dfrac{6}{\sqrt{2}}$	$\dfrac{2}{\sqrt{2}}$
E	6	$2\sqrt{2}$

13. In an experiment to find the capacitance of a capacitor, a student makes the following measurements.

potential difference across capacitor $= (10·0 \pm 0·1)$ V

charge stored by capacitor $= (500 \pm 25)\,\mu C$

Which row in the table gives the capacitance of the capacitor and the percentage uncertainty in the capacitance?

	Capacitance/μF	Percentage uncertainty
A	$0·02$	1
B	$0·02$	5
C	50	1
D	50	5
E	5000	6

14. A capacitor is connected to an a.c. supply and a.c. ammeter as shown.

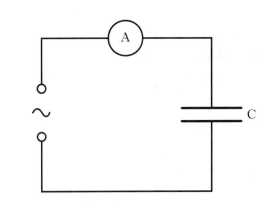

The supply has a constant peak voltage, but its frequency can be varied.

Which graph shows how the current I varies with the frequency f of the supply?

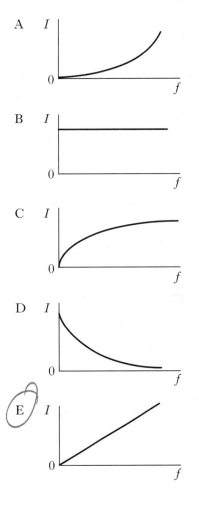

[Turn over

15. Two identical loudspeakers, L_1 and L_2, are connected to a signal generator as shown.

signal generator

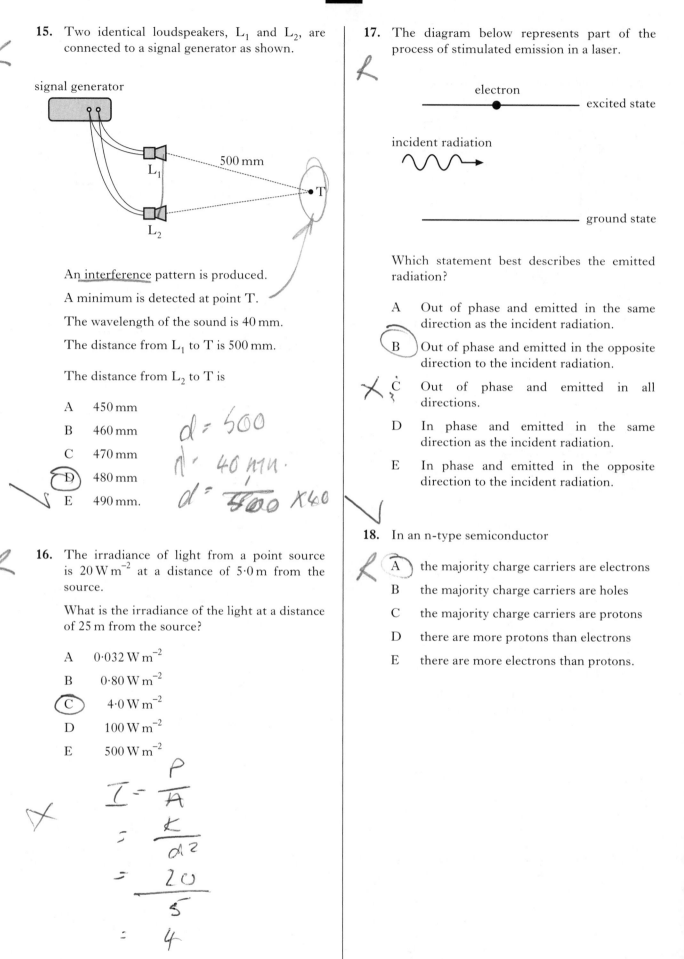

An <u>interference</u> pattern is produced.

A minimum is detected at point T.

The wavelength of the sound is 40 mm.

The distance from L_1 to T is 500 mm.

The distance from L_2 to T is

A   450 mm
B   460 mm
C   470 mm
D   480 mm
E   490 mm.

$d = 500$

$\Lambda = 40\, mm.$

$d = \dfrac{500}{500} \times 40$

16. The irradiance of light from a point source is $20\,\text{W m}^{-2}$ at a distance of $5 \cdot 0\,\text{m}$ from the source.

What is the irradiance of the light at a distance of 25 m from the source?

A $0 \cdot 032\,\text{W m}^{-2}$
B $0 \cdot 80\,\text{W m}^{-2}$
C $4 \cdot 0\,\text{W m}^{-2}$
D $100\,\text{W m}^{-2}$
E $500\,\text{W m}^{-2}$

$I = \dfrac{P}{A}$

$= \dfrac{k}{d^2}$

$= \dfrac{20}{5}$

$= 4$

17. The diagram below represents part of the process of stimulated emission in a laser.

electron
——————●—————— excited state

incident radiation

——————————————— ground state

Which statement best describes the emitted radiation?

A   Out of phase and emitted in the same direction as the incident radiation.

B   Out of phase and emitted in the opposite direction to the incident radiation.

C   Out of phase and emitted in all directions.

D   In phase and emitted in the same direction as the incident radiation.

E   In phase and emitted in the opposite direction to the incident radiation.

18. In an n-type semiconductor

A   the majority charge carriers are electrons

B   the majority charge carriers are holes

C   the majority charge carriers are protons

D   there are more protons than electrons

E   there are more electrons than protons.

19. The following statement represents a nuclear decay.

$$^{214}_{x}\text{Pb} \rightarrow {}^{y}_{83}\text{Bi} + {}^{0}_{z}\text{e}$$

Which row in the table shows the correct values of x, y and z for this decay?

	x	y	z
A	82	210	−1
B	82	214	−1
C	84	214	1
D	85	210	2
E	85	214	2

20. The graph shows how the corrected count rate from a radioactive source varies with the thickness of a material placed between the source and a detector.

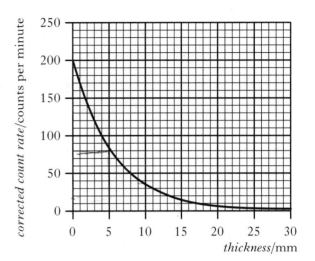

The half value thickness of the material is

A   4 mm

B   14 mm

C   28 mm

D   100 mm

E   200 mm.

[Turn over

SECTION B   *Mark*

Write your answers to questions 21 to 30 in the answer book.

21. A student investigates the motion of a ball projected from a launcher.

μ The launcher is placed on the ground and a ball is fired vertically upwards.

The vertical speed of the ball as it leaves the top of the launcher is $7{\cdot}0\,m\,s^{-1}$.

The effects of air resistance can be ignored.

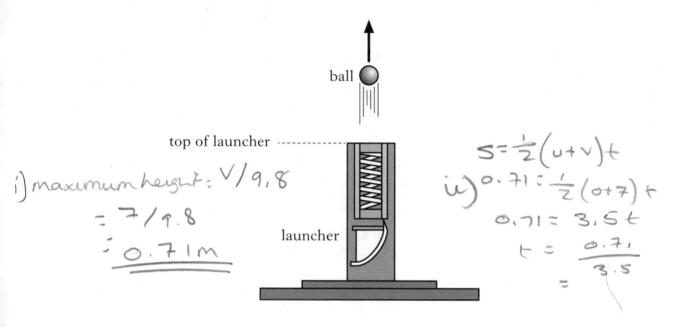

i) maximum height $= V/9.8$
$= 7/9.8$
$= 0.71\,m$

top of launcher

ball

launcher

$s = \frac{1}{2}(u+v)t$

ii) $0.71 = \frac{1}{2}(0+7)t$
$0.71 = 3.5t$
$t = \dfrac{0.71}{3.5}$
$=$

(a)   (i)   Calculate the maximum height above the top of the launcher reached by
the ball.   2

(ii) Show that the time taken for the ball to reach its maximum height is $0{\cdot}71\,s$.   1

Maximum height $= v^2 = u^2 + 2as.$

$v^2 = 7^2 * 2 \times 9.8\,S.$
$0^2 = 49 + 19.6\,S.$

$S = \dfrac{\cancel{68}.}{49/19.6.}$
$= 2.5\,m$

ii) $\dfrac{initial\ velocity}{9.8}$

$= \dfrac{7}{9.8}$

$= 0.71/seconds.$

Marks

21. (continued)

(b) The student now fixes the launcher to a trolley. The trolley travels horizontally at a constant speed of 1·5 m s⁻¹ to the right.

The launcher again fires the ball vertically upwards with a speed of 7·0 m s⁻¹.

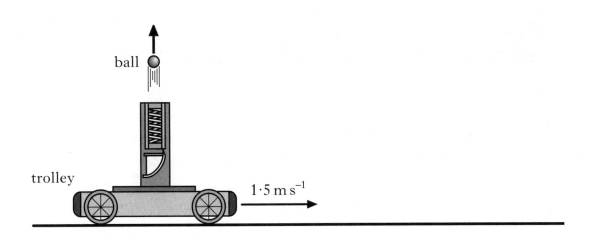

    (i) Determine the velocity of the ball after 0·71 s.   1

   (ii) The student asks some friends to predict where the ball will land relative to the moving launcher. They make the following statements.

Statement X: *The ball will land behind the launcher.*

Statement Y: *The ball will land in front of the launcher.*

Statement Z: *The ball will land on top of the launcher.*

Which of the statements is correct?

You must justify your answer.   2

                                                        (6)

[Turn over

22. An experiment is set up to investigate the motion of a cart as it collides with a force sensor.

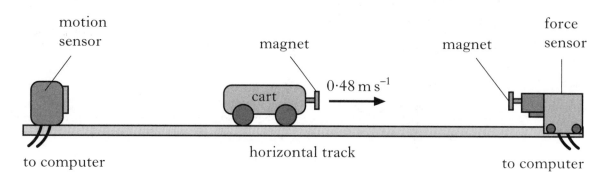

The cart moves along the horizontal track at $0.48\,\text{m s}^{-1}$ to the right.

As the cart approaches the force sensor, the magnets repel each other and exert a force on the cart.

The computer attached to the force sensor displays the following force-time graph for this collision.

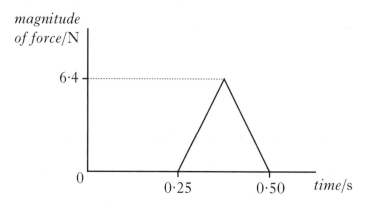

The computer attached to the motion sensor displays the following velocity-time graph for the cart.

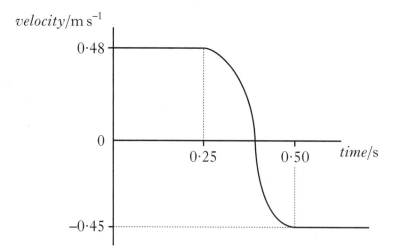

Marks

22. **(continued)**

(*a*) (i) Calculate the magnitude of the impulse on the cart during the collision.   2

   (ii) Determine the magnitude and direction of the change in momentum of the cart.   1

   (iii) Calculate the mass of the cart.   2

(*b*) The experiment is repeated using different magnets which produce a greater average force on the cart during the collision. As before, the cart is initially travelling at $0\cdot48\,\mathrm{m\,s^{-1}}$ to the right and the collision causes the same change in its velocity.

Copy the force-time graph shown and, on the same axes, draw another graph to show how the magnitude of the force varies with time in this collision.

Numerical values are not required but you must label each graph clearly.   2

(7)

[Turn over

Mark

23. A technician uses the equipment shown to calculate a value for the density of air at room temperature.

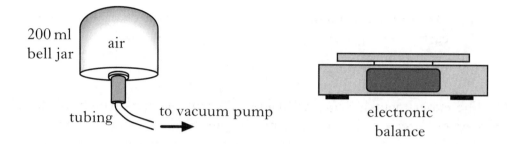

200 ml bell jar | air

tubing   to vacuum pump

electronic balance

The mass of the bell jar is measured when it is full of air. The vacuum pump is then used to remove air from the bell jar. The mass of the bell jar is measured again.

The following measurements are obtained.

Mass before air is removed = 111·49 g

Mass after air is removed = 111·26 g

Volume of bell jar = 200 ml = $2·0 \times 10^{-4} \, m^3$

(a) (i) Use these measurements to calculate a value for the density of air in kg m^{-3}. **(2)**

$d = m/v = 0.23 / 2.0 \times 10^{-4} = 1150 \, kgm^3$

(ii) The accepted value for the density of air at this temperature is 1·29 kg m^{-3}. Explain why the technician's answer is different from the accepted value. **1**

(b) Air is allowed back into the bell jar until it reaches a pressure of $1·01 \times 10^5$ Pa.

The technician now uses a syringe to remove 50 ml of the air from the bell jar.

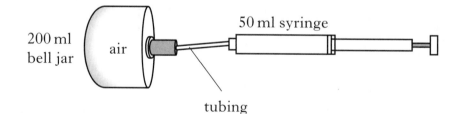

200 ml bell jar | air   50 ml syringe

tubing

The temperature of the air remains constant.

(i) Calculate the new pressure of the air inside the bell jar. **2**

(ii) Use the kinetic model to explain this change in pressure after removing air with the syringe. **2**

(7)

a i) $1150 \, Kgm^{-3}$

ii) Temperature of air can't remain constant all the time. leak of air.

b i) $P_1 V_1 = P_2 V_2$

$(1.01 \times 10^5) \times 200 = P_2 \, 250$

$P_2 = \dfrac{(1.01 \times 10^5) \times 256}{250}$ 8.1×10^4

$= \underline{8.1 \times 10^4 \, Pa}$

Marks

24. (*a*) A supply of e.m.f. 10·0 V and internal resistance *r* is connected in a circuit as shown in Figure 1.

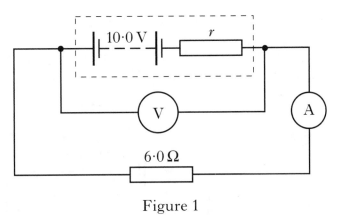

Figure 1

The meters display the following readings.

Reading on ammeter   = 1·25 A

Reading on voltmeter = 7·50 V

   (i) What is meant by an *e.m.f. of 10·0 V*?   **1**

  (ii) Show that the internal resistance, *r*, of the supply is 2·0 Ω.   **1**

(*b*) A resistor R is connected to the circuit as shown in Figure 2.

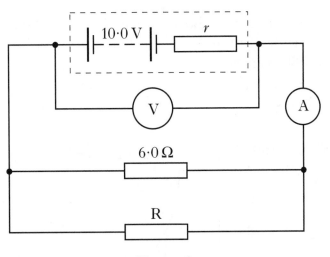

Figure 2

The meters now display the following readings.

Reading on ammeter   = 2·0 A

Reading on voltmeter = 6·0 V

   (i) Explain why the reading on the voltmeter has decreased.   **2**

  (ii) Calculate the resistance of resistor R.   **3**

(7)

Mark

25. A student carries out an experiment using a circuit which includes a capacitor with a capacitance of 200 µF.

(a) Explain what is meant by a *capacitance of 200 µF*.   **1**

(b) The capacitor is used in the circuit shown to measure the time taken for a ball to fall vertically between two strips of metal foil.

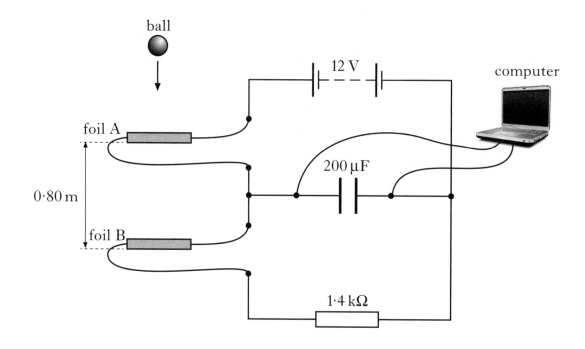

The ball is dropped from rest above foil A. It is travelling at $1.5 \, \text{m s}^{-1}$ when it reaches foil A. It breaks foil A, then a short time later breaks foil B. These strips of foil are $0.80 \, \text{m}$ apart.

The computer displays a graph of potential difference across the capacitor against time as shown.

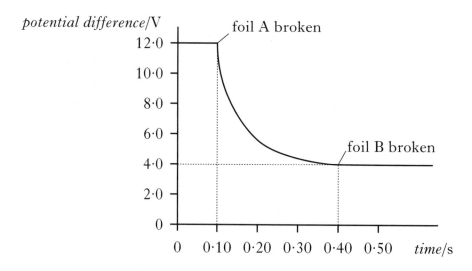

(i) Calculate the current in the $1.4 \, \text{k}\Omega$ resistor at the moment foil A is broken.   **2**

(ii) Calculate the **decrease** in the energy stored in the capacitor during the time taken for the ball to fall from foil A to foil B.   **3**

Marks

25. (continued)

(*c*) The measurements from this experiment are now used to estimate the acceleration due to gravity.

    (i) What is the time taken for the ball to fall from foil A to foil B?   **1**

   (ii) Use the results of this experiment to calculate a value for the acceleration due to gravity.   **2**

  (iii) The distance between the two foils is now increased and the experiment repeated. Explain why this gives a more accurate result for the acceleration due to gravity.   **1**

(10)

[Turn over

Mark

26. (*a*) An op-amp is connected in a circuit as shown.

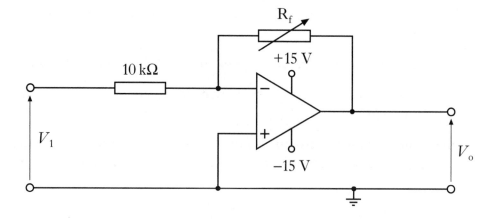

The resistance of the feedback resistor R_f is varied between $20\,k\Omega$ and $120\,k\Omega$.

The graph shows how the output voltage V_o varies as the resistance of the feedback resistor is increased.

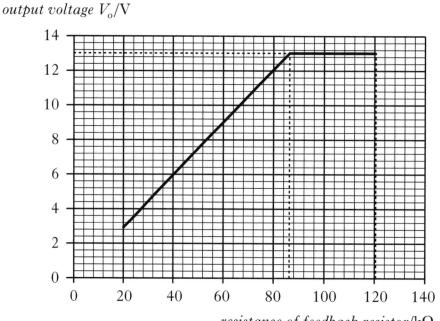

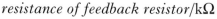

   (i) In which mode is the op-amp being used?   **1**

  (ii) Calculate the input voltage V_1.   **2**

 (iii) Explain why the output voltage V_o does not increase above 13 V.   **1**

Marks

26. (continued)

(*b*) The op-amp is now connected in a different circuit as shown.

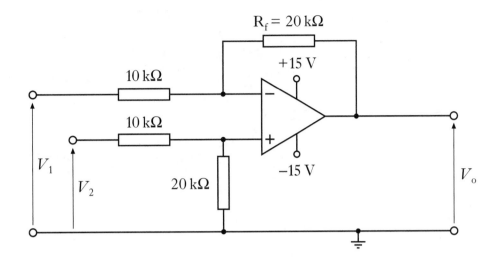

The input voltages V_1 and V_2 are now varied and the corresponding output voltage V_o is measured.

Graph 1 shows the input voltage V_1 for the first 3 seconds.

Graph 2 shows the input voltage V_2 for the first 3 seconds.

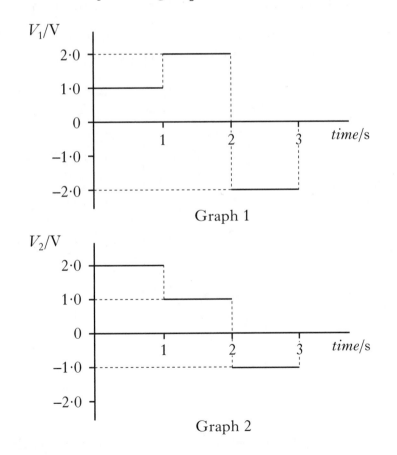

Sketch a graph to show the output voltage V_o from the op-amp for the first 3 seconds.

Numerical values are required on both the voltage and time axes.

3

(7)

Marks

27. (*a*) A ray of red light is incident on a block of glass as shown.

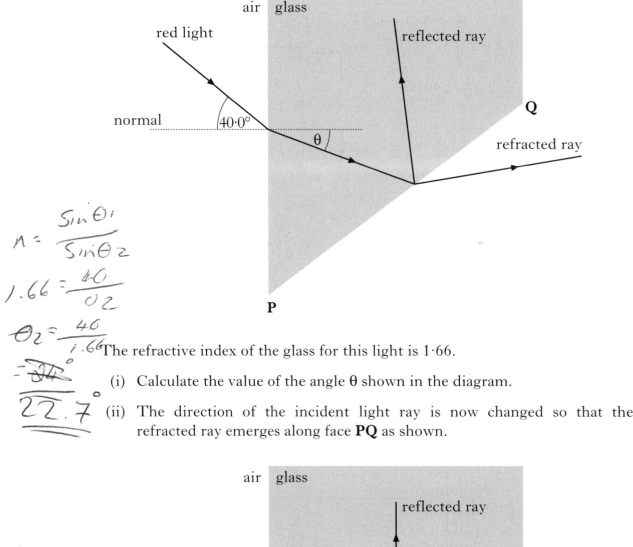

$$n = \frac{\sin \theta_1}{\sin \theta_2}$$

$$1.66 = \frac{40}{\theta_2}$$

$$\theta_2 = \frac{40}{1.66}$$

The refractive index of the glass for this light is 1·66.

$= 24°$

(i) Calculate the value of the angle θ shown in the diagram.   **2**

$22.7°$

(ii) The direction of the incident light ray is now changed so that the refracted ray emerges along face **PQ** as shown.

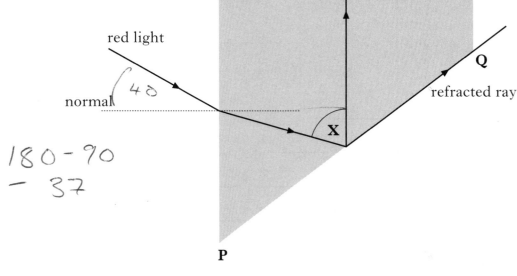

$180 - 90$
$- 37$

(A) Calculate the critical angle for the red light in this glass. $37°$ **2**

(B) Determine the size of angle **X** shown in the diagram. $\longrightarrow 14°$ **1**

Marks

27. **(continued)**

(b) The ray of red light is now replaced with a ray of blue light.

This ray of blue light is directed towards the block along the same path as the ray of red light in part (*a*)(ii).

Is this ray of blue light refracted at face **PQ**?

Justify your answer.   2

                                                                                                                (7)

[Turn over

Mark

28. (*a*) The first demonstration of the interference of light was performed by Thomas Young in 1801.

What does the demonstration of interference prove about light?   **1**

It is a wave. "(light travels as a wave)".

(*b*) A grating is placed in a colourless liquid in a container. Laser light is incident on the grating along the normal. The spacing between the lines on the grating is $5 \cdot 0 \times 10^{-6}$ m. Interference occurs and the maxima produced are shown in the diagram.

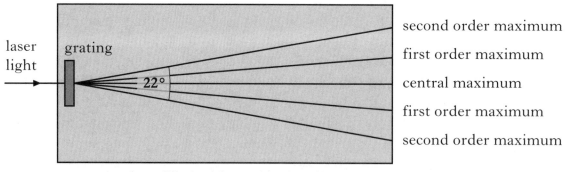

container filled with a colourless liquid

(i) Calculate the wavelength of the laser light in the liquid.   **2**

(ii) The refractive index of the colourless liquid decreases as the temperature of the liquid increases.

The liquid is now heated.

What effect does this have on the spacing between the maxima?

You must justify your answer.   **2**

(5)

29. A metal plate emits electrons when certain wavelengths of electromagnetic radiation are incident on it.

Marks

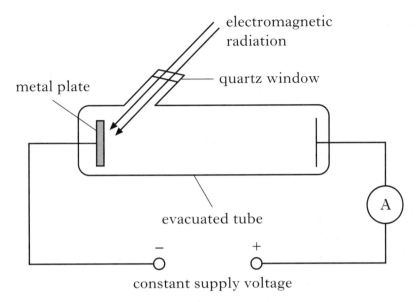

The work function of the metal is $2 \cdot 24 \times 10^{-19}$ J.

(a) Electrons are released when electromagnetic radiation of wavelength 525 nm is incident on the surface of the metal plate.

    (i) Show that the energy of each photon of the incident radiation is $3 \cdot 79 \times 10^{-19}$ J.   **2**

    (ii) Calculate the maximum kinetic energy of an electron released from the surface of the metal plate.   **1**

(b) The frequency of the incident radiation is now varied through a range of values.

The maximum kinetic energy of electrons leaving the metal plate is determined for each frequency.

A graph of this maximum kinetic energy against frequency is shown.

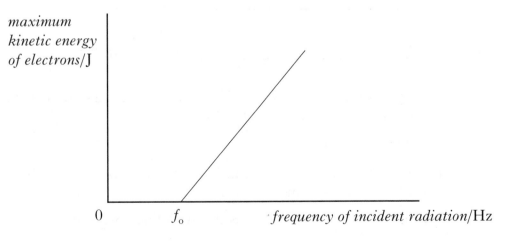

    (i) Explain why the kinetic energy of the electrons is zero below the frequency f_o.   **1**

    (ii) Calculate the value of the frequency f_o.   **2**

                                                                         (6)

[Turn over for Question 30 on *Page twenty-four*

Marks

30. (*a*) The Sun is the source of most of the energy on Earth. This energy is produced by nuclear reactions which take place in the interior of the Sun.

One such reaction can be described by the following statement.

$$\ _{1}^{3}\text{H} + \ _{1}^{2}\text{H} \rightarrow \ _{2}^{4}\text{He} + \ _{0}^{1}\text{n}$$

The masses of the particles involved in this reaction are shown in the table.

Particle	Mass/kg
$_{1}^{3}\text{H}$	$5\cdot005 \times 10^{-27}$
$_{1}^{2}\text{H}$	$3\cdot342 \times 10^{-27}$
$_{2}^{4}\text{He}$	$6\cdot642 \times 10^{-27}$
$_{0}^{1}\text{n}$	$1\cdot675 \times 10^{-27}$

   (i) Name this type of nuclear reaction.   **1**

  (ii) Calculate the energy released in this reaction.   **3**

(*b*) The Sun emits a continuous spectrum of visible light. When this light passes through hydrogen atoms in the Sun's outer atmosphere, certain wavelengths are absorbed.

The diagram shows some of the energy levels for the hydrogen atom.

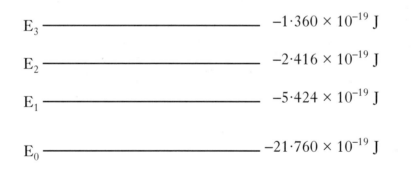

$$E_3 \rule{6cm}{0.4pt} \quad -1\cdot360 \times 10^{-19} \text{ J}$$

$$E_2 \rule{6cm}{0.4pt} \quad -2\cdot416 \times 10^{-19} \text{ J}$$

$$E_1 \rule{6cm}{0.4pt} \quad -5\cdot424 \times 10^{-19} \text{ J}$$

$$E_0 \rule{6cm}{0.4pt} \quad -21\cdot760 \times 10^{-19} \text{ J}$$

   (i) One of the wavelengths absorbed by the hydrogen atoms results in an electron transition from energy level E_1 to E_3.

      Calculate this wavelength.   **3**

  (ii) The absorption of this wavelength produces a faint dark line in the continuous spectrum from the Sun.

      In which colour of the spectrum is this dark line observed?   **1**

                                                                         (8)

[END OF QUESTION PAPER]

[BLANK PAGE]

Acknowledgements

Permission has been sought from all relevant copyright holders and Bright Red Publishing is grateful for the use of the following:
A picture of electronically heated gloves. Reproduced with permission of Zanier Sport (2008 page 15).

HIGHER | ANSWER SECTION

PHYSICS HIGHER
2007

SECTION A

1. D	**2.** C	**3.** B	**4.** D
5. A	**6.** C	**7.** A	**8.** E
9. A	**10.** A	**11.** E	**12.** C
13. D	**14.** A	**15.** E	**16.** C
17. E	**18.** D	**19.** B	**20.** B

SECTION B

21. (a) 350 m at 038°

(b) 5·3 m s^{-1} at 038°

(c) Car Y arrives first because

$$t = \frac{s}{v} = \frac{400}{6 \cdot 5} = 61 \cdot 5 \ (s)$$

(d) 350 m at 218°

22. (a) Component of weight = mgsinθ

$$= 60 \times 9 \cdot 8 \times \sin22(°)$$
$$= 220 \ (N)$$

(b) Unbalanced force: $= 220 - 180 = 40$ N

Acceleration: $a = \frac{F}{m} = \frac{40}{60} = 0 \cdot 67$ m s^{-2}

(c) $v^2 = u^2 + 2as$

$$= 0 + (2 \times 0 \cdot 67 \times 50)$$
$$= 8 \cdot 2 \ m \ s^{-1}$$

(d) Smaller mass causes
- smaller component of weight
- smaller unbalanced force
- smaller acceleration
- smaller speed at the bottom of the slope

23. (a) $P_1V_1 = P_2V_2$

$$750 \times 8 \cdot 0 \times 10^{-2} = 125 \times V$$
$$= 0 \cdot 48 \ m^3$$

(b) Volume of gas available $= 0 \cdot 48 - 0 \cdot 08 = 0 \cdot 40$ m^3

Number of balloons $= \frac{0 \cdot 40}{0 \cdot 02} = 20$

(c)
- As *mass* of the helium gas is <u>constant</u> from the cylinder into the balloons
- then as the <u>volume increases</u>
- and as density = *mass* ÷ *volume* ($\rho = \frac{m}{V}$)
- then <u>density</u> must <u>decrease</u> in the balloons.

24. (a) At A, $E_k = \frac{1}{2}mv^2$

$$= \frac{1}{2} \times 6 \cdot 64 \times 10^{-27} \times (2 \cdot 60 \times 10^6)^2$$
$$= 2 \cdot 24 \times 10^{-14} \ (J)$$

Increase in E_k = work done between the plates

$$= 3 \cdot 05 \times 10^{-14} - 2 \cdot 24 \times 10^{-14}$$
$$= 8 \cdot 1 \times 10^{-15} \ (J)$$

(b) $\qquad$ W = QV

$$8 \cdot 1 \times 10^{-15} = 3 \cdot 2 \times 10^{-19} \times V$$
$$V = 2 \cdot 5 \times 10^4 \ V$$

(c) Same potential difference
But the charge is smaller
so less work is done.
so smaller (increase in) kinetic energy.

25. (a) 12 V

(b) (i) $\quad$ E = V + Ir

$$12 = 9 \cdot 6 + (I \times 2.0)$$
$$2 \cdot 4 = I \times 2 \cdot 0$$
$$I = \frac{2 \cdot 4}{2 \cdot 0} = 1 \cdot 2 \ A$$

$\quad$ (ii) $\ R = \frac{V}{I} = \frac{9 \cdot 6}{1 \cdot 2} = 8 \ \Omega$

(c) $\quad$ *p.d.*/V

26. (a) $I = \frac{V}{R}$

$$= \frac{12}{480000}$$
$$= 2 \cdot 5 \times 10^{-5} \ A$$

(b) $V_C = 12 - 3 \cdot 8 = 8 \cdot 2$ V

$$Q = CV$$
$$= 2200 \times 10^{-6} \times 8 \cdot 2$$
$$= 1 \cdot 8 \times 10^{-2} \ C$$

(c) $E = \frac{1}{2}CV^2$

$$= \frac{1}{2} \times 2200 \times 10^{-6} \times 12^2$$
$$= 0 \cdot 16 \ J$$

27. (a) $\frac{X}{R_{Th}} = \frac{Y}{Z}$

$$\frac{2200}{R_{Th}} = \frac{5000}{750}$$
$$R_{Th} = 330 \ \Omega$$

(b) (i) Differential (mode)

$\quad$ (ii) As temperature decreases:
- voltage across Z decreases/voltage at Q decreases/voltage across thermistor increases

- potential at Q decreases
- potential difference between P and Q increases.
- amplified (by the op amp)
- MOSFET/transistor switches on/ conducts when voltage reaches threshold/certain/ sufficiently high voltage.

$\quad$ (iii) $V_o = \frac{R_f}{R_1} (V_2 - V_1)$

$$3 \cdot 0 = \frac{100}{40} (V_2 - V_1)$$
$$3 \cdot 0 = 2 \cdot 5 \times V_{PQ}$$
$$V_{PQ} = 1 \cdot 2 \ V$$

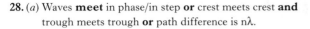

28. (a) Waves **meet** in phase/in step **or** crest meets crest **and** trough meets trough **or** path difference is $n\lambda$.

    (b) (i)   (A) mean value for distance AB = 1·10 m

             (B) approximate random uncertainty = 0·01 m

       (ii)   % AB = $(\frac{0\cdot01}{1\cdot10} \times 100)$ = 0·9%

           % BC = $(\frac{10}{270} \times 100)$ = 3·7%

           (BC has the larger percentage uncertainty)

       (iii) $n\lambda = d \sin\theta$

$$2 \times \lambda = 4\cdot00 \times 10^{-6} \times \frac{0\cdot270}{1\cdot10}$$

$$\lambda = 4\cdot91 \times 10^{-7} \text{ (m)}$$

3·7% of $4\cdot91 \times 10^{-7} = 0\cdot18 \times 10^{-7}$

$$\lambda = (4\cdot91 \times 10^{-7} \pm 0\cdot18 \times 10^{-7}) \text{ m}$$

29. (a) $\dfrac{\sin\theta_1}{\sin\theta_2} = n$

$$\frac{\sin 50^{(\circ)}}{\sin\theta_2} = 1\cdot50$$

$$\theta_2 = 31°$$

    (b) $n = \dfrac{\lambda_1}{\lambda_2}$

$$1\cdot50 = \frac{\lambda_1}{420}$$

$$\lambda_1 = 1\cdot50 \times 420$$

$$= 630 \text{ nm}$$

    (c) Blue light has a higher/larger/different frequency
Due to a different/larger refractive index,
it refracts more/at a greater/different angle.

30. (a) $f_o = \dfrac{v}{\lambda} = \dfrac{3 \times 10^8}{605 \times 10^{-9}} = 4\cdot96 \times 10^{14}$ Hz

$$E = hf_o$$

$$= 6\cdot63 \times 10^{-34} \times 4\cdot96 \times 10^{14}$$

$$= 3\cdot29 \times 10^{-19} \text{ J}$$

OR

$$E = h\frac{v}{\lambda}$$

$$= \frac{6\cdot63 \times 10^{-34} \times 3 \times 10^8}{605 \times 10^{-9}}$$

$$= 3\cdot29 \times 10^{-19} \text{ (J)}$$

    (b) (i) $E_k = 5\cdot12 \times 10^{-19} - 3\cdot29 \times 10^{-19}$

            $= 1\cdot83 \times 10^{-19}$ J

       (ii) Current/Ammeter reading decreases as irradiance decreases.
This is because there are fewer photons hitting the plate per second so fewer electrons are released (one electron per photon).

31. (a) Decrease in mass =
$398\cdot626 \times 10^{-27} - (391\cdot970 \times 10^{-27} + 6\cdot645 \times 10^{-27})$

       $= 1\cdot1 \times 10^{-29}$ (kg)

       $E = mc^2$

          $= 1\cdot1 \times 10^{-29} \times (3 \times 10^8)^2$

          $= 9\cdot9 \times 10^{-13}$ J

    (b) $D = 4\cdot0 \times 10^{-6} \times 2 = 8\cdot0 \times 10^{-6}$ Gy

       $H = D\, w_R = 8\cdot0 \times 10^{-6} \times 3 = 24\ \mu\text{Sv}$

HIGHER PHYSICS
2008

SECTION A

1. D	2. A	3. B	4. C
5. D	6. C	7. D	8. E
9. E	10. D	11. A	12. B
13. E	14. C	15. A	16. B
17. B	18. C	19. C	20. D

SECTION B

21. (a) $v^2 = u^2 + 2as$

$$12^2 = 30^2 + (2 \times -9 \times s)$$

$$s = 42 \text{ m}$$

    (b) Speed at Q is greater/faster because:
- Deceleration/acceleration is less
- Mass of car is greater/bigger
- $a = F/m$ (and F is constant)

    (c) (i) electrons and holes recombine at/in the junction (and energy is released)

       (ii) $V_r = 12 - 5 = 7$ V

$$I = \frac{P}{V}$$

$$= \frac{2\cdot2}{5} = 0\cdot44 \text{ (A)}$$

$$R = \frac{V}{I}$$

$$= \frac{7}{0\cdot44}$$

$$= 16\ \Omega$$

22. (a) (i) $F = mg \sin\theta$

$$= 40 \times 9\cdot8 \times \sin 30$$

$$= 196 \text{ N}$$

       (ii) Balanced forces
          or
          F = $mg \sin\theta$ + Frictional force
          240   = $196 + F_f$
          F_f = 44 N

    (b) (i) Constant deceleration (of 6 m s^{-2})
         or Constant acceleration (of -6 m s^{-2})

       (ii)

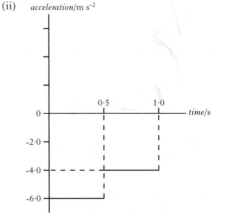

       (iii) When crate moving up the slope, mgsinθ/comp of weight and friction are in the same direction.
Moving back down the slope, forces are in opposite direction or friction has changed direction.

23. (a) (i) $\dfrac{P_1}{T_1} = \dfrac{P_2}{T_2}$

$\dfrac{2 \cdot 82 \times 10^6}{(19 + 273)} = \dfrac{P_2}{(5 + 273)}$

$P_2 = 2 \cdot 68 \times 10^6$ Pa

(ii) No change as both mass <u>and</u> volume remain constant and density = mass/volume ($\rho = m/V$)

(b) (i) $m = \rho V$

$m = 37 \cdot 6 \times 0 \cdot 03$

$m = 1 \cdot 13$ kg

(ii) Fewer molecules/atoms/particles inside canister so fewer collisions/hits **with walls** per second.

(iii) (gas stops escaping when) pressure inside = pressure outside

or

gas has reached atmospheric pressure

or

because $1 \cdot 01 \times 10^5$ Pa = atmospheric pressure

24. (a) (i) $4\ \Omega$

(ii) $I = \dfrac{E}{R_{(T)}}$ or $\dfrac{V}{R}$

$= \dfrac{2 \times 1 \cdot 5}{4}$

$= 0 \cdot 75$ A

(iii) $P = I^2 R$

$= 0 \cdot 75^2 \times 3 \cdot 6$

$= 2 \cdot 0$ W

(b) Power output is less because:

$P = I^2 R$

Current is less

R (load) is constant

or

$P = \dfrac{V^2}{R}$

t.p.d./V is less

R (load) is constant

or

$P = IV$

Current is less

t.p.d./V is also less

25. (a) Quantity of charge stored per volt

or

Coulombs per volt

or

ratio of charge to p.d./voltage

(b) (i) $3 \cdot 4$ V

(ii) $R = V/I$

$= 3 \cdot 4/0 \cdot 0016$

$= 2125\ \Omega$

(iii) $V = 12$ V from diagram

$E = \dfrac{1}{2} C V^2$

$10 \cdot 8 \times 10^{-3} = \dfrac{1}{2} \times C \times 12^2$

$C = 0 \cdot 00015$ F

(c) Time is less as

• Circuit resistance is less

• Current/rate of flow of charge is greater

26. (a) $\dfrac{R_1}{R_2} = \dfrac{R_3}{R_4}$ so $\dfrac{R_{ldr}}{1 \cdot 2} = \dfrac{6}{4}$ so $R_{ldr} = 1 \cdot 8$ (kΩ)

From graph, irradiance = $0 \cdot 48$ W m^{-2}

(b) (i) $\dfrac{2 \cdot 0}{2 \cdot 0 + 1 \cdot 2} \times 12 = 7 \cdot 5$ V

$Or\ I = \dfrac{V}{R_t} = \dfrac{12}{(1200 + 2000)} = 0 \cdot 00375$ A

$V = I \times R_{ldr}$

$= 0 \cdot 00375 \times 2000$

$= 7 \cdot 5$ V

(ii) $V_O = (V_2 - V_1)\dfrac{R_f}{R_1}$

$= (7 \cdot 2 - 7 \cdot 5) \times \dfrac{140}{20}$

$= -2 \cdot 1$ V

(iii) Yellow LED is lit

because it is **forward biased**.

27. (a) (i) $\dfrac{\sin \theta_a}{\sin \theta_g} = n$

$\dfrac{\sin 28}{\sin \theta_g} = 1 \cdot 61$

$\theta_g = 17°$

(ii) $\lambda_{(air)} = \dfrac{v_{(air)}}{f}$

$= \dfrac{3 \times 10^8}{4 \cdot 8 \times 10^{14}}$

$\lambda_g = \dfrac{\lambda_{(air)}}{n}$

$= \dfrac{6 \cdot 25 \times 10^{-7}}{1 \cdot 61}$

$= 3 \cdot 88 \times 10^{-7}$ m

(b) Ray will pass through point X because refractive index for blue light > refractive index for red light **or** blue light refracted more.

28. (a) Power = 40/20 = 2 mW

$P = I \times A$

$2 \times 10^{-3} = I \times 8 \times 10^{-5}$

$I = 25$ W m^{-2}

(b) For point source, $I_1 \times d_1^2 = I_2 \times d_2^2$

or

$I_1 \times d_1^2 = 1 \cdot 1 \times 0 \cdot 5^2 = 0 \cdot 28$

$I_2 \times d_2^2 = 0 \cdot 8 \times 0 \cdot 7^2 = 0 \cdot 39$

$I_3 \times d_3^2 = 0 \cdot 6 \times 0 \cdot 9^2 = 0 \cdot 49$

Values are not equal - not a point source.

29. (a) *Energy/E/hf*

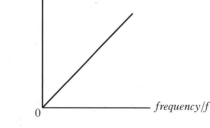

(b) $E = hf$

$= 6 \cdot 63 \times 10^{-34} \times 6 \cdot 1 \times 10^{14}$

Photon energy = WF + E_k

WF = $4 \cdot 044 \times 10^{-19} - 6 \times 10^{-20}$

$= 3 \cdot 44 \times 10^{-19}$ J

(c) Each photon still has same amount of energy.

30. (a) (i) 12 000 decays per second.

    (ii) aluminium – 2 half values
        lead – 3 half values
        800 -- 400 -- 200 -- 100 -- 50 -- 25
        count rate = 25 counts per second.

  (b) (i) $0\cdot03\ \mu$Sv

    (ii) $\dfrac{60}{0\cdot03} = 2000$

PHYSICS HIGHER 2009

SECTION A

1. B	**2.** C	**3.** B	**4.** D
5. C	**6.** A	**7.** C	**8.** D
9. C	**10.** B	**11.** C	**12.** A
13. C	**14.** D	**15.** E	**16.** B
17. D	**18.** E	**19.** A	**20.** E

SECTION B

21. (a) (i) $u_h = 6\cdot5 \cos 50° = 4\cdot2\ \mathrm{m\,s^{-1}}$

    (ii) $u_v = 6\cdot5 \sin 50° = 5\cdot0\ \mathrm{m\,s^{-1}}$

  (b) $t = \dfrac{s}{v}$

       $= \dfrac{2\cdot9}{4\cdot2}$

       $= 0\cdot69$ (s)

  (c) $s = ut + \frac{1}{2}at^2$

       $= 5 \times 0\cdot69 + \frac{1}{2} \times -9\cdot8 \times (0\cdot69)^2$

       $= 1\cdot1$ (m)

    so height $h = 2\cdot3 + 1\cdot1 = 3\cdot4$ m

  (d) Ball would **not** land in basket

    (initial) vertical speed would increase

    So ball is higher than the basket when it has travelled 2·9 m horizontally

    or

    So ball has travelled further horizontally when it is at the same height as the basket

22. (a) (i) (A)

      $\text{mean} = \dfrac{248 + 259 + 251 + 263 + 254}{5}$

           $= 255\ \mu$s

    (B) uncertainty $= \dfrac{263 - 248}{5}$

                $= (\pm)\ 3\ \mu$s

    (ii) (mean contact time $= 255 \pm 3\ \mu$s)

       max value $= 258\ \mu$s

       club does **not** meet standard

  (b) (i) $F = \dfrac{mv - mu}{t}$

       $= \dfrac{4\cdot5 \times 10^{-2} \times (50 - 0)}{450 \times 10^{-6}}$

       $= 5000$ N

    (ii) Impulse on the ball is greater
       or
       $\underline{\Delta}$mv is greater
       So speed increased

23. (a) (i) $P \times V$ = 2000 1995 2002 2001
all 4 values needed

$P \times V$ = constant

or $P \times V$ = 2000

or $P_1 V_1 = P_2 V_2$

or $P = k/V$

(ii) Gas <u>molecules</u> <u>collide</u> with <u>walls</u> of container more
often so (average) force increases
pressure increases

(b) (i) pressure due to <u>water</u>

P = $\rho g h$
= $1020 \times 9 \cdot 8 \times 12$
= 120000 (Pa)

Total pressure = $120000 + 1 \cdot 01 \times 10^5$
= $2 \cdot 21 \times 10^5$ (Pa)

(ii) $P_1 V_1 = P_2 V_2$

$1 \cdot 01 \times 10^5 \times 1 \cdot 50 \times 10^{-3} = 2 \cdot 21 \times 10^5 \times V_2$

$V_2 = 6 \cdot 86 \times 10^{-4}$ m³

(c) pressure decreases as $P = \rho g h$
volume of air in lungs will increase
(or pressure difference increases)
so <u>lungs</u> may become damaged

24. (a) (i) $V_{tpd} = IR$
= $1 \cdot 5 \times 3$
= $4 \cdot 5$ (V)

lost volts = $E - V_{tpd}$
= $6 \cdot 0 - 4 \cdot 5$
= $1 \cdot 5$ V

(ii) $r = \dfrac{lost\ volts}{I}$

$= \dfrac{1 \cdot 5}{3 \cdot 0}$

$= 0 \cdot 5\ \Omega$

or

$r = \dfrac{E}{I}$

$= \dfrac{6 \cdot 0}{12}$

$= 0 \cdot 5\ \Omega$

or

$E = IR + Ir$

$6 \cdot 0 = (3 \times 1 \cdot 5) + (3 \times r)$

$r = 0 \cdot 5\ \Omega$

(b) current decreases

so lost volts ($V = Ir$) decreases

25. (a) (i) $V_P = 3 \times 0 \cdot 5 = 1 \cdot 5$ mV

(ii) $f = \dfrac{1}{T}$

$= \dfrac{1}{4 \times 10^{-3}}$

= 250 Hz

(b) (i) inverting (mode)

(ii) $V_{rms} = \dfrac{V_{peak}}{\sqrt{2}}$

$= \dfrac{6 \cdot 2 \times 10^{-3}}{\sqrt{2}}$

$= 4 \cdot 38 \times 10^{-3}$ (V)

$\dfrac{V_O}{V_I} = -\dfrac{R_f}{R_1}$

$\dfrac{V_O}{4 \cdot 38 \times 10^{-3}} = -\dfrac{10 \times 10^6}{5 \times 10^3}$

V_O = (−) 8·8 V

(iii) trace will be "clipped"/flattened (at ± 9 V) or <u>almost</u>
square wave
max output voltage will be ± 9 V/V_s
or op-amp saturates
or saturation occurs

26. (a)   (Current)

(b) $V_R = IR$
= $5 \times 10^{-3} \times 500$
= $2 \cdot 5$ (V)

V_C = $12 - 2 \cdot 5$
= $9 \cdot 5$ V

(c) $E = \dfrac{1}{2} C V^2$
= $0 \cdot 5 \times 47 \times 10^{-6} \times 12^2$
= $3 \cdot 4 \times 10^{-3}$ J

(d) Max energy the same/ 'no effect'
Values of "C" <u>and</u> "V" are same as before

27. (a) waves <u>meet</u> out of phase
or crest meets trough
or path difference = $(n + \frac{1}{2}) \lambda$

(b) $\lambda_{blue\ light}$ is shorter (than $\lambda_{red\ light}$)
and $n \lambda = d \sin\theta$
or
$\sin\theta = n \lambda / d$

(c) $n \lambda = d \sin\theta$
$2 \times 4 \cdot 73 \times 10^{-7} = 2 \cdot 00 \times 10^{-6} \sin\theta$
$\theta = 28 \cdot 2°$

28. (a) (i) $E_3 \rightleftharpoons E_0$

$(\Delta)E \propto f$ **or** $E = hf$

$f \propto \dfrac{1}{\lambda}$ **or** $v = f\lambda$

(ii) $(\Delta)E = hf$ or $W_2 - W_1 = hf$

$-5 \cdot 2 \times 10^{-19} - (-9 \cdot 0 \times 10^{-19}) = 6 \cdot 63 \times 10^{-34} \times f$

$f = 5 \cdot 7 \times 10^{14}$ Hz

(b) $\lambda_a = \left(\dfrac{v}{f}\right) = \dfrac{3 \times 10^8}{4 \cdot 6 \times 10^{14}}$

$= 6 \cdot 5 \times 10^{-7}$ (m)

$\dfrac{\lambda_a}{\lambda_g} = \dfrac{\sin \theta_a}{\sin \theta_g}$

$\dfrac{6 \cdot 5 \times 10^{-7}}{\lambda_g} = \dfrac{\sin 53^\circ}{\sin 30^\circ}$

$\lambda_g = 4 \cdot 1 \times 10^{-7}$ m

29. (a) (i) $E_k = hf - hf_0$

$= 5 \cdot 23 \times 10^{-19} - 2 \cdot 56 \times 10^{-19}$

$= 2 \cdot 67 \times 10^{-19}$ J

(ii) $E_k = \dfrac{1}{2}mv^2$

$2 \cdot 67 \times 10^{-19} = \dfrac{1}{2} \times 9 \cdot 11 \times 10^{-31} \times v^2$

$v = 7 \cdot 66 \times 10^5 \text{ ms}^{-1}$

(b) No change (to maximum speed)/no effect
Energy/frequency of photons does not change
or
Energy an electron receives is the same

30. (a) (i) $r = 95$

$s = 7$

(ii) Total mass of reactants

> total mass of products

or

(there is a) loss of mass

(iii) Total mass before

$= 390 \cdot 173 \times 10^{-27} + 1 \cdot 675 \times 10^{-27}$

$= 3 \cdot 91848 \times 10^{-25}$ (kg)

Total mass after

$= 230 \cdot 584 \times 10^{-27} + 157 \cdot 544 \times 10^{-27} +$

$(2 \times 1 \cdot 675 \times 10^{-27})$

$= 3 \cdot 91478 \times 10^{-25}$ (kg)

$\Delta m = 3 \cdot 91848 \times 10^{-25} - 3 \cdot 91478 \times 10^{-25}$

$= 3 \cdot 7 \times 10^{-28}$ (kg)

$E = mc^2$

$= 3 \cdot 7 \times 10^{-28} \times (3 \times 10^8)^2$

$= 3 \cdot 3 \times 10^{-11}$ J

(b) (i) 12 mm

(ii) $200 \rightarrow 100 \rightarrow 50$

2 half-value thicknesses

$= 2 \times 12 = 24$ mm

PHYSICS HIGHER 2010

SECTION A

1. E	2. E	3. D	4. A
5. D	6. B	7. C	8. B
9. A	10. D	11. D	12. C
13. E	14. A	15. B	16. D
17. E	18. D	19. B	20. C

See also the extra note sheets.

SECTION B

21. (a) (i) 47 km
156$^{(o)}$
or 24° east of south
or 66° south of east

(ii) $v = s/t$
$v = (47100$ **or** $47000)/900$
$v = 52 \cdot 3$ **or** $52 \cdot 2 \text{ ms}^{-1}$
[**or** 188 km h^{-1}]
at 156$^{(o)}$

(b) (i) Lift $= mg$ **or** lift $=$ weight
or forces balanced
$W = 1 \cdot 21 \times 10^4 \times 9 \cdot 8$
$W = 119$ kN

(ii) Weight is less
There is a resultant force upwards **or** unbalanced force upwards **or** net force upwards

Upward Acceleration

OR

The helicopter accelerates upwards

weight is less
there is a net upward force

22. (a) (i) The total momentum before (a collision) equals the total momentum after (the collision)

'In the absence of external forces'
or 'in an isolated system'

(ii) $m_A u_A + m_B u_B = m_A v_A + m_B v_B$
$(0 \cdot 22 \times 0 \cdot 25) + 0.16u = (0 \cdot 38 \times 0 \cdot 2)$
$0 \cdot 055 + 0 \cdot 16u = 0 \cdot 076$
$u = 0.13 \text{ ms}^{-1}$

(b) The find velocity is less
because the (total initial) momentum is less,
the mass is constant
and v = momentum/mass

23. (a) (i) $v^2 = u^2 + 2as$
$v^2 = 0^2 + 2 \times 9 \cdot 8 \times 2$
$v = \underline{6 \cdot 3} \text{ (m s}^{-1})$
or
$(m)gh = \frac{1}{2}(m)v^2$
$v = \sqrt{(2 \times 9 \cdot 8 \times 2)}$
$v = \underline{6 \cdot 3} \text{ (m s}^{-1})$

(ii) $(\Delta p) = m(v - u)$
$= 40(-5.7 - 6.3)$
$= -480 \text{ kg m s}^{-1}$

or

$(\Delta p) = m(v - u)$
$= 40(5.7 - (-6.3))$
$= 480 \text{ kg m s}^{-1}$

(iii) $F = \Delta p / t$
$F = (-)480/0{\cdot}5$
$F = (-)960$ N

(b) Weight/downwards force is constant
vertical component(s) balances weight

as angle increases tension must increase
because $T = \frac{1}{2} W / \cos \theta$

24. (a) (i) $0{\cdot}51$ s

(ii) Random uncertainty = {max – min} / no.
= {$0{\cdot}55 - 0{\cdot}49$}/6
= $0{\cdot}01$ s

(b) (i) $Q = CV$
$Q = 1{\cdot}6 \times 10^{-3} \times 4{\cdot}5$
$Q = 7{\cdot}2 \times 10^{-3}$ C

(ii) ($I = V/R$
$I = 4{\cdot}5/18000$
$I = 0{\cdot}25$ mA)

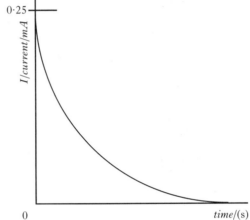

25. (a) (i) $R_1/R_2 = R_3/R_4$
$R_1 = 6000 \times 800/4000$
$R_1 = 1200\ \Omega$

(ii) $V_P = 4{\cdot}0$ V
$V_Q = 4{\cdot}8$ V
Voltmeter reading = $0{\cdot}8$ V

(b) $V_o = (V_2 - V_1)\ (R_f/R_1)$
$V_o = (3{\cdot}2 - 3{\cdot}0)\ (2{\cdot}0 \times 10^6/20 \times 10^3)$
$V_o = 20$ (V)

(But, due to saturation, the actual output voltage is)
10 to 12 V

26. (a) (i) $V_p = 2{\cdot}0$ V

(ii) $f = 1/T$
$f = 1/0{\cdot}01$
$f = 100$ Hz

(b) Stays the same/constant/no change/nothing

(c) increases/doubles

(d) The capacitor will be damaged
The peak voltage from this power supply is greater than 16
V because $V_P = \sqrt{2} \times 15 = 21{\cdot}2$ V

27. (a) $S_2P - S_1P = (n + \frac{1}{2})\ \lambda$
$0{\cdot}34 = \lambda/2$
$\lambda = 0{\cdot}68$ m

or

path difference = $\frac{1}{2}\ \lambda$
path difference = $0{\cdot}34$ m
$\lambda = 0{\cdot}68$ m

(b) The amplitude increases **or** is greater
because <u>destructive</u> interference is no longer taking place

28. (a) (i) $P = F/A$
$F = 4{\cdot}6 \times 10^5 \times 3{\cdot}00 \times 10^{-2}$
$F = 13800$ N

(ii) $P_1V_1 = P_2V_2$
$4{\cdot}6 \times 10^5 \times 1{\cdot}6 \times 10^{-3} = 1{\cdot}0 \times 10^5 \times V_2$
$V_2 = 7{\cdot}36 \times 10^{-3}$ (m^3)
V of water = $(7{\cdot}36 - 1{\cdot}6) \times 10^{-3}$
$= 5{\cdot}76 \times 10^{-3}\ m^3$

(b) (i) Stays the same/constant/nothing/no change

(ii) $n = \sin \theta_1/\sin \theta_2$
$n = \sin 60/\sin 41$
$n = 1{\cdot}32$

(iii) $\sin \theta_C = 1/n$
$\sin \theta_C = 1/1{\cdot}32$
$\theta_C = 49°$

(iv) The critical angle is less
because the refractive index is larger

29. (a) Very small area/diameter/radius (of beam)
$I = P/A$ **or** High irradiance

(b) $E = hf$
$E = 6{\cdot}63 \times 10^{-34} \times 4{\cdot}74 \times 10^{14}$
$E = 3{\cdot}14 \times 10^{-19}$ J

(c) Frequency/wavelength/energy
Direction
Speed
Phase/coherent
Velocity

(d) $\lambda = v/f = 3 \times 10^8/4{\cdot}74 \times 10^{14} = 633$ (nm)
$n\lambda = d \sin \theta$
$d = (2 \times 633 \times 10^{-9})/\sin 30$
$d = 2{\cdot}5 \times 10^{-6}$ m

30. (a) 146

(b) (i) $r = 93$
$s = 237$

(ii) $T = $ Neptunium (**or** Np)

(c) $N = At$
$N = 30 \times 10^3 \times 60$
$N = 1{\cdot}8 \times 10^6$

(d) $I = V/R$
$I = 5/16$
$I = 0{\cdot}3125$ (A)

$E = I(R + r)$
$9 = 0{\cdot}3125\ (R + 2)$
$9 = 0{\cdot}3125R + 0{\cdot}625$
$8{\cdot}375 = 0{\cdot}3125R$
$R = 26{\cdot}8\ \Omega$

$R = 26{\cdot}8 - 16 = 10{\cdot}8 = 11\ \Omega$

or

$I = V/R$
$I = 5/16$
$I = 0{\cdot}3125$ (A)

$V_{lost} = Ir = 2 \times 0{\cdot}3125 = 0{\cdot}625$ (V)

$V_{resistor} = 9 - (5 + 0{\cdot}625) = 3{\cdot}375$ (V)

$R = V/I$
$R = 3{\cdot}375/0{\cdot}3125$
$R = 10{\cdot}8 = 11\Omega$

or

$I = V/R$
$\quad = 5/16$
$\quad = 0{\cdot}3125$ (A)

$R_T = E/I$
$\quad\quad = 9/0{\cdot}3125$
$\quad\quad = 28{\cdot}8\Omega$

$R = R_T - 18 = 28.8 - 18$
$\quad\quad = 10.8 = 11\Omega$

PHYSICS HIGHER 2011

SECTION A

1. C	**2.** E	**3.** C	**4.** A
5. C	**6.** D	**7.** A	**8.** E
9. C	**10.** B	**11.** B	**12.** A
13. D	**14.** E	**15.** D	**16.** B
17. D	**18.** A	**19.** B	**20.** A

SECTION B

21. (*a*) (i) $v^2 = u^2 + 2as$
$\quad\quad 0 = 7^2 + 2 \times (-9{\cdot}8) \times s$
$\quad\quad s = \textbf{2·5}\ \text{m}$

or
$\quad v = u + at$
$\quad 0 = 7 + (-9{\cdot}8)\,t$
$\quad t = 0{\cdot}71\ \text{s}$

$\quad s = ut + \tfrac{1}{2} a t^2$

$\quad\quad = 7 \times 0{\cdot}71 + \tfrac{1}{2}(-9{\cdot}8)(0{\cdot}71)^2$

$\quad\quad = \textbf{2·5}\ \text{m}$

(ii) $v = u + at$
$\quad 0 = 7 + (-9{\cdot}8) \times t$
$\quad t = \textbf{0·71}\ \text{s}$

or
$\quad s = \left(\dfrac{u + v}{2}\right) t$

$\quad 2{\cdot}5 = \left(\dfrac{7 + 0}{2}\right) \times t$

$\quad t = \textbf{0·71}\ \text{s}$

(*b*) (i) $1{\cdot}5\ \text{m s}^{-1}$ to the **right**

(ii) Statement Z

Horizontal speed of ball remains constant and equal to (horizontal) speed of trolley
or
Horizontal speed of the ball remains constant at $1{\cdot}5\ \text{m s}^{-1}$

22. (*a*) (i) *Impulse = Area under F–t graph*

$\quad\quad = \tfrac{1}{2}\,6{\cdot}4 \times 0{\cdot}25$

$\quad\quad = \textbf{0·80}\ \text{kg m s}^{-1}$

(ii) **0·80** kg m s^{-1}
in the negative direction **or** to the left

(iii) *(Impulse = Change in momentum)*
$\quad F \times t = mv - mu$
$\quad -0{\cdot}80 = m\,(-0{\cdot}45 - 0{\cdot}48)$
$\quad m = \textbf{0·86}\ \text{kg}$

(*b*)

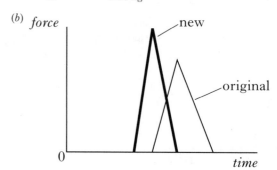

23. (*a*) (i) $m = 111\cdot49 - 111\cdot26$

$= 0\cdot23$ g

$\rho = m/V$

$= 0\cdot23 \times 10^{-3}/2\cdot0 \times 10^{-4}$

$= \mathbf{1\cdot15}$ kg m^{-3}

(ii) Not all the air will be evacuated from jar

or

It is impossible to get a (perfect) vacuum

or

Some air has leaked back in

(*b*) (i) $P_1V_1 = P_2V_2$

$1\cdot01 \times 10^5 \times 200 = P_2 \times 250$

$P_2 = \mathbf{8\cdot1 \times 10^4}$ Pa

(ii) <u>Particles collide</u> with <u>walls</u> of jar
So when air is removed, number of collisions on walls of jar is less frequent/less often and average force (on walls) decreases, and pressure on walls of jar decreases

24. (*a*) (i) 10 joules of energy are given to each coulomb (of charge) passing through the supply

(ii) $I = \dfrac{E}{(R + r)}$

$1\cdot25 = \dfrac{10}{(6 + r)}$

$r = \mathbf{2\cdot0}\ \Omega$

or

$r = \dfrac{lost\ volts}{I}$

$= \dfrac{10 - 7\cdot5}{1\cdot25}$

$= 2\cdot0\ \Omega$

or

$\dfrac{R_1}{R_2} = \dfrac{V_1}{V_2}$

$\dfrac{r}{6\cdot0} = \dfrac{2\cdot5}{7\cdot5}$

$r = \mathbf{2\cdot0}\ \Omega$

(*b*) (i) (Total) resistance decreases
(circuit) current increases
lost volts increases

(ii) Parallel resistance $= R = V/I$

$= 6\cdot0/2\cdot0$

$= 3\cdot0\ \Omega$

$1/R_T = 1/R_1 + 1/R_2$
$1/3 = 1/6 + 1/R$
$R = \mathbf{6\cdot0}\ \Omega$

or

Total resistance $= E/I$

$= 10/2\cdot0$

$= 5\cdot0\ \Omega$

Resistance of parallel network $= 5 - 2$

$= 3\ \Omega$

$R_T = \dfrac{Product}{Sum}$

$3 = \dfrac{6 \times R}{6 + R}$

$R = \mathbf{6\cdot0}\ \Omega$

25. (*a*) 200 μC of charge increases voltage across plates by 1 volt

or

200 μC per volt

or

One volt across the plates of the capacitor causes 200 μC of charge to be stored

(*b*) (i) $I = E/R$

$= 12/1400$

$= \mathbf{0\cdot0086}$ A

$(\mathbf{8\cdot6\ mA})$

(ii) $E = \frac{1}{2}\,CV^2$

initial stored energy $= \frac{1}{2} \times (200 \times 10^{-6}) \times 12^2$

$= 0\cdot0144$ J

final stored energy $= \frac{1}{2}\,(200 \times 10^{-6}) \times 4^2$

$= 0\cdot0016$ J

Difference $= 0\cdot0144 - 0\cdot0016$

decrease in stored energy $= \mathbf{0\cdot0128}$ J

(*c*) (i) $0\cdot30$ s

(ii) $s = ut + \frac{1}{2}\,a\,t^2$

$0\cdot80 = 1\cdot5 \times 0\cdot3 + \frac{1}{2} \times a \times (0\cdot3)^2$

$a = \mathbf{7\cdot8}$ m s^{-2}

(iii) Percentage (fractional) uncertainty in (measuring) <u>distance</u> will be smaller

or

Percentage (fractional) uncertainty in (measuring) <u>time</u> will be smaller

26. (*a*) (i) Inverting

(ii) $V_o = -\dfrac{R_f}{R_1} \times V_1$

$12 = \dfrac{-80}{10} \times V_1$

$V_1 = \mathbf{-1\cdot5}$ V

(iii) Output cannot be greater than (approx 85% of) the supply voltage

or

Saturation <u>of the amplifier</u> has been reached

(*b*) V_o/V

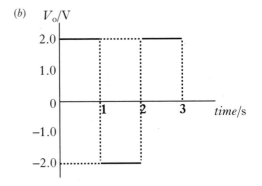

27. (a) (i) $n = \dfrac{\sin \theta_1}{\sin \theta_2}$

$1 \cdot 66 = \dfrac{\sin 40}{\sin \theta}$

$\theta = \mathbf{22 \cdot 8°}$

(ii) (A) $\sin \theta_C = 1/n$

$= 1/1 \cdot 66$

$\theta_C = 37 \cdot 0°$

(B) 74°

(b) No

or

it is totally internally reflected $\Big\}$

and

n depends on frequency

or

$n_{blue} > n_{red}$

or

blue refracts more than red $\Big\}$

and

(critical angle) $_{blue}$ < (critical angle) $_{red}$

or

the angle of incidence has increased $\Big\}$

and

angle of incidence of blue light on face PQ is greater than the critical angle

28. (a) Light travels as waves

or

Energy in light is carried as a wave

or

Light is a wave

(b) (i) $d\sin\theta = n\lambda$

$5 \times 10^{-6} \times \sin 11 = 2 \times \lambda$

$\lambda = \mathbf{480}$ nm

(ii) Spacing of maxima increases

λ in liquid increases
(as n decreases)

$\sin\theta = n\lambda/d$

θ increases

29. (a) (i) $f = \dfrac{c}{\lambda}$

$= \dfrac{3 \cdot 00 \times 10^8}{525 \times 10^{-9}}$

$= 5 \cdot 71 \times 10^{14}$ Hz

$E = hf$

$= 6 \cdot 63 \times 10^{-34} \times 5 \cdot 71 \times 10^{14}$

$= \mathbf{3 \cdot 79 \times 10^{-19}}$ J

(ii) $\Big(E_k = hf - hf_o$

$= 3 \cdot 79 \times 10^{-19} - 2 \cdot 24 \times 10^{-19}\Big)$

$= \mathbf{1 \cdot 55 \times 10^{-19}}$ J

(b) (i) <u>Photons</u> with frequency below f_o do not have enough <u>energy</u> to release electrons

or

<u>Photons</u> with frequency below f_o have <u>energy</u> smaller than work function

(ii) Work function $= hf_o$ (**or** $E = hf_o$)

$2 \cdot 24 \times 10^{-19} = (6 \cdot 63 \times 10^{-34}) \times f_o$

$f_o = \mathbf{3 \cdot 38 \times 10^{14}}$ Hz

30. (a) (i) (Nuclear) Fusion

(ii) Total mass before

$= 3 \cdot 342 \times 10^{-27} + 5 \cdot 005 \times 10^{-27}$

$= 8 \cdot 347 \times 10^{-27}$ (kg)

Total mass after

$= 6 \cdot 642 \times 10^{-27} + 1 \cdot 675 \times 10^{-27}$

$= 8 \cdot 317 \times 10^{-27}$ (kg)

Loss in mass $= 0 \cdot 030 \times 10^{-27}$ (kg)

Energy released $= mc^2$

$= 0 \cdot 030 \times 10^{-27} \times (3 \cdot 00 \times 10^8)^2$

$= \mathbf{2 \cdot 7 \times 10^{-12}}$ J

(b) (i) Energy absorbed

$= -1 \cdot 360 \times 10^{-19} - (-5 \cdot 424 \times 10^{-19})$

$= 4 \cdot 064 \times 10^{-19}$ (J)

$E = hf$

$4 \cdot 064 \times 10^{-19} = 6 \cdot 63 \times 10^{-34} \times f$

$f = 6 \cdot 13 \times 10^{14}$ (Hz)

$\lambda = \dfrac{c}{f}$

$= \dfrac{3 \cdot 00 \times 10^8}{6 \cdot 13 \times 10^{14}}$

$= \mathbf{489}$ nm

(ii) 'Blue' **or** 'blue-green'

© 2011 SQA/Bright Red Publishing Ltd, All Rights Reserved
Published by Bright Red Publishing Ltd, 6 Stafford Street, Edinburgh, EH3 7AU
Tel: 0131 220 5804, Fax: 0131 220 6710, enquiries: sales@brightredpublishing.co.uk,
www.brightredpublishing.co.uk

Official SQA answers to 978-1-84948-224-0
2007-2011